II030017

ANALYTICAL QUADRICS

by

BARRY SPAIN

Analytical Quadrics by Dr. Spain, head of the Mathematics Department of Sir John Cass College, is intended to serve as a concise introduction to the analytical geometry of three dimensions.

The book begins by developing *ab initio* the theory of the plane, straight line, sphere, cone and cylinder, central quadrics and paraboloids in their standard forms. Next, the concept of the plane at infinity is introduced with the aid of homogeneous Cartesian co-ordinates and applied to the nature of the intersection of three planes and to the circular sections of quadrics. Subsequently, the properties of the quadric given by the general equation are studied. After this, the invariants of a quadratic form under translations and rotations are treated and applied to the classification and reduction of the quadric. This is followed by a discussion of foci, confocals and linear systems of quadrics. Finally, an introductory treatment is presented of plane co-ordinates leading to the general treatment of confocal systems. The concept of the rank of a matrix has been widely used. The definition of a matrix and all the results required are summarized in the first appendix.

This authoritative volume will undoubtedly be given the same enthusiastic reception as Dr. Spain's previous volume in the series, *Analytical Conics*.

INTERNATIONAL SERIES OF MONOGRAPHS ON

PURE AND APPLIED MATHEMATICS

GENERAL EDITORS: I. N. SNEDDON, S. ULAM and M. STARK

Volume 11

AXIOMATICS OF
CLASSICAL STATISTICAL MECHANICS

OTHER TITLES IN THE SERIES
ON PURE AND APPLIED MATHEMATICS

Vol. 1. WALLACE—*Introduction to Algebraic Topology*

Vol. 2. PEDOE—*Circles*

Vol. 3. SPAIN—*Analytical Conics*

Vol. 4. MIKHLIN—*Integral Equations*

Vol. 5. EGGLESTON—*Problems in Euclidean Space: Applications of Convexity*

Vol. 6. WALLACE—*Homology Theory on Algebraic Varieties*

Vol. 7. NOBLE—*Methods Based on the Wiener–Hopf Technique for the Solution of Partial Differential Equations*

Vol. 8. MIKUSINSKI—*Operational Calculus*

Vol. 9. HEINE—*Group Theory in Quantum Mechanics*

Vol. 10. BLAND—*The Theory of Linear Viscoelasticity*

Vol. 12. FUCHS—*Abelian Groups*

Vol. 13. KURATOWSKI—*Introduction to Set Theory and Topology*

Vol. 14. SPAIN—*Analytical Quadrics*

Vol. 15. HARTMAN and MIKUSINSKI—*Theory of Measure and Lebesgue Integration*

Vol. 16. KULCZYCKI—*Non-Euclidean Geometry*

Vol. 17. KURATOWSKI—*Introduction to Calculus*

AXIOMATICS OF CLASSICAL STATISTICAL MECHANICS

RUDOLF KURTH

Department of Mathematics
The Durham Colleges in the University of Durham

PERGAMON PRESS

OXFORD · LONDON · NEW YORK · PARIS

1960

PERGAMON PRESS LTD.
Headington Hill Hall, Oxford
4 & 5 Fitzroy Square, London W.1

PERGAMON PRESS INC.
122 East 55th Street, New York 22, N.Y.
P.O. Box 47715, Los Angeles, California

PERGAMON PRESS S.A.R.L.

24 Rue des Écoles, Paris Vᵉ

PERGAMON PRESS G.m.b.H.
Kaiserstrasse 75, Frankfurt am Main

Library of Congress Card Number 60-8973

Printed in Great Britain by John Wright & Sons Ltd., Bristol

By the same author:

Von den Grenzen des Wissens (Basel, 1953)
Zum Weltbild der Astronomie (with M. Schürer) (Bern, 1954)
Entwurf einer Metaphysik (Bern, 1955)
Christentum und Staat (Bern, 1957)
Introduction to the Mechanics of Stellar Systems (London, 1957)
Introduction to the Mechanics of the Solar System (London, 1959)

"Wer dem Gange einer höheren Erkenntnis und Einsicht getreulich folgt, wird zu bemerken haben, dass Erfahrung und Wissen fortschreiten und sich bereichern können, dass jedoch das Denken und die eigentlichste Einsicht keineswegs in gleichem Maasse vollkommen wird, und zwar aus der ganz natürlichen Ursache, weil das Wissen unendlich und jedem neugierig Umherstehenden zugänglich, das Überlegen, Denken und Verknüpfen aber innerhalb eines gewissen Kreises der menschlichen Fähigkeiten eingeschlossen ist."

GOETHE, *Annalen*, 1804

PREFACE

THIS book is an attempt to construct classical statistical mechanics as a deductive system, founded only on the equations of motion and a few well-known postulates which formally describe the concept of probability. This is the sense in which the word "axiomatics" is to be understood. An investigation of the compatibility, independence and completeness of the axioms has not been made: their compatibility and independence appear obvious, and completeness, in its original simple sense, is an essential part of the *mos geometricus* itself and, in fact, of the scientific method in general: all the assumptions of the theory have to be stated explicitly and completely. (I know there are other interpretations of the word "completeness", but I cannot help feeling them to be artificial.)

The aim adopted excluded some subjects which are usually dealt with in books on statistical mechanics, in particular the theory of Boltzmann's equation; it has not been and cannot be derived from the above postulates, as is shown by the contradiction between Boltzmann's H-Theorem and Poincaré's Recurrence Theorem. By this statement I do not wish to deny the usefulness of Boltzmann's equation; I wish only to emphasize that it cannot be a part of a rational system founded on the above assumptions. Instead, it constitutes a separate theory based on a set of essentially different hypotheses.

My aim demanded that the propositions of the theory be formulated *more geometrico* also, that is, in the form "if ..., then ...", which, in my opinion, is the only appropriate form for scientific propositions. For convenience in derivation or formulation the assumptions were sometimes made less general than they could have been.

It was intended to make the book as self-contained as possible. Therefore the survey of the mathematical tools in Chapter II was included so that only the elements of calculus and analytical geometry are supposed to be known by the reader. In order to confine this auxiliary chapter to suitable

vii

proportions, however, full proofs were given only in the simplest cases, while lengthier or more difficult proofs were only sketched or even omitted altogether. Thus, in this respect, I have achieved only a part of my aim.

The set of the references given is the intersection of the set of writings I know by my own study and the set of writings which appeared relevant for the present purpose. A part of the text is based on investigations of my own, not all of which have yet been published.

It is a pleasure for me to remember gratefully the encouragement I received from Dr. D. ter Haar (now at Oxford University) and Professor E. Finlay-Freundlich (at St. Andrews University) when I made the first steps towards the present essay and had to overcome many unforeseen obstacles. Several colleagues at Manchester University were so kind as to correct my English. Particularly, I am indebted to Dr. H. Debrunner (Princeton) for his many most valuable criticisms of my manuscript. Last but not least, I gratefully acknowledge that it was A. J. Khinchin's masterly book which gave me the courage to think for myself in statistical mechanics, after a long period of doubt about the conventional theory. To them all I offer my best thanks.

Cheadle (*Cheshire*)   RUDOLF KURTH

CONTENTS

I. INTRODUCTION

1. Statement of the Problem 1

II. MATHEMATICAL TOOLS

2. Sets 3
3. Mapping 7
4. Point Sets in the n-dimensional Vector Space R^n . 9
5. Topological Mapping in Vector Spaces . . . 16
6. Systems of Ordinary Differential Equations . . 18
7. The Lebesgue Measure 24
8. The Lebesgue Integral 29
9. Hilbert Spaces 38
   References 45

III. THE PHASE FLOWS OF MECHANICAL SYSTEMS

10. Mechanical Systems 47
11. Phase Flow; Liouville's Theorem 52
12. Stationary Measure-conserving Phase Flow;
    Poincaré's, Hopf's and Jacobi's Theorems . . 57
13. The Theorems of v. Neumann and Birkhoff; The
    Ergodic Hypothesis 66
    References 76

IV. THE INITIAL DISTRIBUTION OF PROBABILITY IN THE PHASE SPACE

14. A Formal Description of the Concept of Probability 77
15. On the Application of the Concept of Probability . 80
    References 87

V. PROBABILITY DISTRIBUTIONS WHICH DEPEND ON TIME

16. Mechanical Systems with General Equations of
    Motion 88
17. Hamiltonian and Newtonian Systems . . . 93
18. The Initial Value Problem 103
19. The Approach of Mechanical Systems towards
    States of Statistical Equilibrium . . . 110
    References 119

VI. TIME-INDEPENDENT PROBABILITY DISTRIBUTIONS

20. Fluctuations in Statistical Equilibrium . . . 121
21. Gibbs's Canonic Probability Distribution . . 129
    References 141

VII. STATISTICAL THERMODYNAMICS

22. The Equation of State 142
23. The Fundamental Laws of Thermodynamics . . 153
24. Entropy and Probability 165
    References 175

INDEX 177

CHAPTER I

INTRODUCTION

§ 1. Statement of the problem

In this book we shall consider mechanical systems of a finite number of degrees of freedom of which the equations of motion read

$$\dot{x}_i = X_i(x, t), \qquad i = 1, 2, ..., n. \qquad (*)$$

t is the time variable; dots denote differentiation with respect to t, the x_i's, $i = 1, 2, ..., n$, are Cartesian coordinates of the n-dimensional vector space R^n, which is also called the phase-space Γ of the system; x is the vector or "phase-point" $(x_1, x_2, ..., x_n)$, and the $X_i(x, t)$'s are continuous functions of (x, t) defined for all values of (x, t). Further, we assume that, for each point $\overset{0}{x}$ of Γ and at each moment t, there is a uniquely determined solution

$$x_i = \chi_i(\overset{0}{x}, \overset{0}{t}, t), \qquad i = 1, 2, ..., n, \qquad (**)$$

of the system of differential equations (*) which satisfies the initial conditions

$$\overset{0}{x}_i = \chi_i(\overset{0}{x}, \overset{0}{t}, \overset{0}{t}), \qquad i = 1, 2, ..., n.$$

Then the principal problem of mechanics reads: *for a given "force" $X(x, t)$ and a given initial condition $(\overset{0}{x}, \overset{0}{t})$, to calculate or to characterize qualitatively the solution* (**). In this formulation, the problem of general mechanics appears as a particular case of the initial value problem of the theory of ordinary differential equations. It is, in fact, a particular case since mechanics imposes certain restrictions on the functions $X_i(x, t)$ which are not assumed in the general theory of differential equations. (Cf. §§ 6 and 10.)

If the number n of equations (*) and unknown functions (**) is very large, two major difficulties arise. First, the initial phase-point $\overset{0}{x}$ of a real system can no longer be actually determined by observation. (It is, for example, impossible to observe

1

the initial positions of all the molecules of a gas or of all the stars of a galaxy.) Secondly, even if the initial point $\overset{\circ}{x}$ of such a system is known, the actual computation of the solution (**) is no longer practicable, not even approximately by numerical methods.

But it is just this embarrassingly large number n which provides a way out, at least under certain conditions which will be given fully later: it now becomes possible to describe the average properties of these solutions, and it seems plausible to apply such "average solutions" in all cases in which, for any reason, the individual solutions cannot be known.

The average behaviour of mechanical systems is the subject of statistical mechanics. Its principal problems, therefore, read: *to define suitable concepts of the average properties of the solutions* (**), *to derive these average properties from the equations of motion* (*); *and to vindicate their application to individual systems.* Before starting this programme in Chapter III, the principal mathematical tools which are required will be discussed in Chapter II.

MATHEMATICAL TOOLS

§ 2. Sets

2.1. "A *set* is a collection of different objects, real or intellectual, into a whole." ("Eine Menge ist die Zusammenfassung verschiedener Objekte unserer Anschauung oder unseres Denkens zu einem Ganzen"—CANTOR.) This sentence is not to be understood as a definition, but rather as the description of an elementary intellectual act or of the result of this act. Since it is an *elementary* act, which cannot be reduced to any other act or fact in our mind, the description cannot be other than vague. Nevertheless, everyone knows perfectly what is meant by, for instance, an expression such as "the set of the vertices of a triangle".

The objects collected in a set are called its *elements* and we say: "the elements form or make the set", "they belong to it", "the set consists of the elements", "it contains these elements", etc. The meaning of terms such as "element of", "forms", "consists of", etc., is supposed to be known. The sentence, "s is an element of the set S", is abbreviated symbolically by the formula $s \in S$, and the sentence "the set S consists of the elements $s_1, s_2, \ldots$" by the formula $S = \{s_1, s_2, \ldots\}$.

It is formally useful to admit sets consisting of only one element (though there is nothing like "collection" or "Zusammenfassung") and even to admit a set containing no element at all. The latter set is called an *empty set*.

2.2. DEFINITIONS. A set S_1 is called a *subset* of a set S if each element of S_1 is contained in S. For this we write $S_1 \subseteq S$ or $S \supseteq S_1$. If there is at least one element of S which does not belong to S_1, the set S_1 is called a *proper subject* of the set S. In this case, we write $S_1 \subset S$ or $S \supset S_1$. If for two sets S_1 and S_2 the relations $S_1 \subseteq S_2$ and $S_2 \subseteq S_1$ are valid at the same time, both sets are called *equal* and we write $S_1 = S_2$. The empty set is regarded as a subset of every set.

A set is called *finite* if it consists of a finite number of elements. Otherwise it is called *infinite*. A set is called *enumerable* if there is an ordinal number (in the ordinary sense) for each element and, conversely, an element for each ordinal number, i.e. if there is a one-to-one correspondence between the elements of the set and the ordinal numbers. A *sequence* is defined as a finite or enumerable ordered set, i.e. a finite or enumerable set given in a particular enumeration. If any two elements of a sequence are equal (for example, numerically) they are still distinguished by the position within the sequence; thus, as members of the sequence, they are to be considered as different.

Let $\{S_1 S_2 \dots\}$ be a set (or, as we prefer to say for linguistic reasons, an aggregate) of sets $S_1, S_2, \dots$; then the *sum* $(S_1 + S_2 + \dots)$ of the sets $S_1, S_2, \dots$ is defined as the set of all the elements contained in at least one of the sets $S_1, S_2, \dots$. If the aggregate $\{S_1, S_2, \dots\}$ is finite or enumerable we denote the sum $(S_1 + S_2 + \dots)$ also by $\sum\limits_{\nu=1}^{n} S_\nu$ or $\sum\limits_{\nu=1}^{\infty} S_\nu$.

The *intersection* $S_1 S_2 \dots$ or $S_1 . S_2 \dots$ of the sets $S_1, S_2, \dots$ is defined as the set of all the elements contained in each of the sets $S_1, S_2, \dots$. If the aggregate $\{S_1, S_2, \dots\}$ is finite or enumerable, the intersection is also denoted by $\prod\limits_{\nu=1}^{n} S_\nu$ or $\prod\limits_{\nu=1}^{\infty} S_\nu$.

The (*Cartesian*) *product* $S_1 \times S_2 \times \dots$ of the sets of a finite or enumerable aggregate of sets $S_1, S_2, \dots$ is defined as the aggregate of all the sequences $\{s_1, s_2, \dots\}$ where s_1 is any element of S_1, etc. (Example: the square $0 \leqslant x \leqslant 1$, $0 \leqslant y \leqslant 1$ of the (x, y) plane is the Cartesian product of both its sides $0 \leqslant x \leqslant 1$ and $0 \leqslant y \leqslant 1$.)

Let S_1 be a subset of S. Then the set of all the elements of S which are not contained in S_1 is called the *difference*, $S - S_1$, of both sets.

The operations which produce sums, intersections, Cartesian products or differences of sets will be called (set) addition, intersection, (Cartesian) multiplication or subtraction.

If all the sets occurring in a theory are subsets of a given fixed set S, this set S is called a *space*. Let S_1 be a subset of a space S. Then the difference $S - S_1$ is called the *complement* S_1^* of the set S_1.

An aggregate A of subsets $S_1, S_2, \ldots$ of a space S is called an *additive class* if it satisfies the following conditions:

(i) S is an element of A;

(ii) if S_1 is an element of A, then the complement $S_1^* = S - S_1$ is also an element of A;

(iii) if each set $S_1, S_2, \ldots$ of a finite or enumerable aggregate $\{S_1, S_2, \ldots\}$ of sets $S_1, S_2, \ldots$ is an element of A, then the sum $S_1 + S_2 + \ldots$ is also an element of A.

Example. The aggregate of all the subsets of the space S is an additive class.

2.3. THEOREMS. *The addition and intersection of the sets of a finite or infinite system of sets $S_1, S_2, \ldots$ are associative and commutative.* Thus, in particular,

$$(S_1 + S_2) + S_3 = S_1 + (S_2 + S_3),$$

$$(S_1 S_2) S_3 = S_1 (S_2 S_3)$$

(so that we may write without any brackets $S_1 + S_2 + S_3$ and $S_1 S_2 S_3$ for $(S_1 + S_2) + S_3$ and $(S_1 S_2) S_3$) and

$$S_1 + S_2 = S_2 + S_1,$$

$$S_1 S_2 = S_2 S_1.$$

For the following pairs of set-operations the distributive law holds: addition and intersection, subtraction and intersection, addition and Cartesian multiplication, subtraction and Cartesian multiplication. Thus,

$$(S_1 + S_2) S_3 = S_1 S_3 + S_2 S_3,$$

$$(S_2 - S_1) S_3 = S_2 S_3 - S_1 S_3,$$

$$\left. \begin{aligned} (S_1 + S_2) \times S_3 &= (S_1 \times S_3) + (S_2 \times S_3), \\ S_3 \times (S_1 + S_2) &= (S_3 \times S_1) + (S_3 \times S_2), \end{aligned} \right\}$$

$$\left. \begin{aligned} (S_2 - S_1) \times S_3 &= (S_2 \times S_3) - (S_1 \times S_3), \\ S_3 \times (S_2 - S_1) &= (S_3 \times S_2) - (S_3 \times S_1). \end{aligned} \right\}$$

These statements can be made intuitively evident by figures of the following kind:

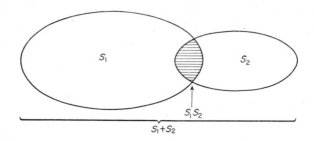

2.4. THEOREM. *Let* $\{S_1, S_2, \ldots\}$ *be a finite or enumerable aggregate of finite or enumerable sets* $S_1, S_2, \ldots$. *Then the sum* $S_1 + S_2 + \ldots$ *is a finite or enumerable set.*

Proof. Write

$$S_1 = \{s_{11}, s_{12}, s_{13}, \ldots\},$$

$$S_2 = \{s_{21}, s_{22}, s_{23}, \ldots\},$$

$$S_3 = \{s_{31}, s_{32}, s_{33}, \ldots\},$$

$$\text{---} \cdot$$

Then the sequence $\{s_{11}, s_{12}, s_{21}, s_{13}, s_{22}, s_{31}, s_{14}, s_{23}, \ldots\}$ yields an enumeration of $S_1 + S_2 + \ldots$. (The elements having already occurred in the enumeration have to be omitted.)

2.5. THEOREM. *The set of all rational numbers is enumerable.*

Proof. The set of all rational numbers can be represented as the sum of the following enumerable sets:

$$S_{+1} = \{+\tfrac{1}{1}, +\tfrac{1}{2}, +\tfrac{1}{3}, +\tfrac{1}{4}, \ldots\},$$

$$S_{-1} = \{-\tfrac{1}{1}, -\tfrac{1}{2}, -\tfrac{1}{3}, -\tfrac{1}{4}, \ldots\},$$

$$S_{+2} = \{+\tfrac{2}{1}, +\tfrac{2}{2}, +\tfrac{2}{3}, +\tfrac{2}{4}, \ldots\},$$

$$S_{-2} = \{-\tfrac{2}{1}, -\tfrac{2}{2}, -\tfrac{2}{3}, -\tfrac{2}{4}, \ldots\},$$

$$\text{---} \cdot$$

Now apply Theorem 2.4.

2.6. THEOREM. *Let $S_1, S_2, \ldots$ be subsets of a space S, and let the complement of a set be denoted by an asterisk. Then*

$$(S_1 + S_2 + \ldots)^* = S_1^* S_2^* \ldots,$$
$$(S_1 S_2 \ldots)^* = S_1^* + S_2^* + \ldots.$$

Proof. Let s be an element of $(S_1 + S_2 + \ldots)^*$, and denote by the symbol $\notin$ the negation of the relation $\in$. Then

$$s \in (S_1 + S_2 + \ldots)^*,$$
$$s \notin S_1 + S_2 + \ldots,$$
$$s \notin S_1, \quad s \in S_2, \ldots,$$
$$s \in S_1^*, \quad s \in S_2^*, \ldots,$$
$$s \in S_1^* S_2^* \ldots.$$

Hence $\qquad (S_1 + S_2 + \ldots)^* \subseteq S_1^* S_2^* \ldots.$

By inverting the chain of arguments, it follows that

$$S_1^* S_2^* \ldots \subseteq (S_1 + S_2 + \ldots)^*,$$

and both inequalities together imply the first statement. The proof of the second one is similar.

2.7. THEOREM. *Let $\{S_1, S_2, \ldots\}$ be a finite or enumerable aggregate of sets belonging to an additive class A. Then the intersection $S_1 S_2 \ldots$ is an element of A.*

Proof.

$$S_1 S_2 \ldots = S - (S_1 S_2 \ldots)^* = S - (S_1^* + S_2^* + \ldots)$$

(by Theorem 2.6).

Since $S_1^*, S_2^*, \ldots$ and, therefore, $(S_1^* + S_2^* + \ldots)$ are elements of A, it follows that $S_1 S_2 \ldots = (S_1^* + S_2^* + \ldots)^*$ is an element of A, too.

§ 3. Mapping

3.1. DEFINITIONS. Let X and Y be two sets (which need not be different), and suppose that to each element x of X there corresponds a unique element y of Y. (The same element of Y may correspond to different elements of X.) Then we write $y = f(x)$ where $x \in X$, and say: y or $f(x)$ is a *function* of x defined in the set X; the set X is *mapped* into the set Y; and the set of elements $f(x)$ which correspond to the elements x

of X is the *image* of the set X. It is denoted by $f(X)$. If $f(X) = Y$ (so that each element y of Y is the image $f(x)$ of at least one element x of X), then the set X is said to be *mapped on* the set Y by the function $f(x)$.

Like the word "collection" (Zusammenfassung) in 2.1, the word "correspondence" denotes an elementary act of our mind which, by its nature, does not admit of a formal definition.

If $f(x)$ is a function defined in a set X such that $f(x_1) \neq f(x_2)$ for $x_1 \neq x_2$, then the function (or the mapping) f is said to be *bi-uniform*. If $Y = f(X)$ is the bi-uniform image of X, then to each element y of Y there corresponds exactly one element x of X such that $y = f(x)$. This correspondence is called the *inverse function* of the function f and is denoted by f^{-1}.

3.2. THEOREM. *Let $f(x)$ be a function defined in a set X. Then, for any subsets $X_1, X_2, \ldots$ of X,*

$$f(X_1 + X_2 + \ldots) = f(X_1) + f(X_2) + \ldots,$$

$$f(X_1 X_2 \ldots) \subseteq f(X_1) f(X_2) \ldots,$$

and, if $X_2 \supseteq X_1$, $f(X_2 - X_1) \supseteq f(X_2) - f(X_1)$.

Proof. From

$$f(X_1) \subseteq f(X_1 + X_2 + \ldots),$$

$$f(X_2) \subseteq f(X_1 + X_2 + \ldots),$$

––––––––––––––

it follows that

$$f(X_1) + f(X_2) + \ldots \subseteq f(X_1 + X_2 + \ldots).$$

Conversely, if $x \in X_1 + X_2 \ldots$, then x belongs to at least one of the sets X_1, X_2, and, therefore, $f(x)$ belongs to at least one of the sets $f(X_1), f(X_2), \ldots$.

Hence $f(X_1 + X_2 + \ldots) \subseteq f(X_1) + f(X_2) + \ldots$.

This yields, together with the above inequality, the first statement. The proofs of the other statements are similar.

3.3. THEOREM. *Let $f(x)$ be a bi-uniform function defined in the set X. Then, for any subsets $X_1, X_2, \ldots$ of X,*

$$f(X_1 X_2 \ldots) = f(X_1) \cdot f(X_2), \ldots,$$

and, if $X_2 \supseteq X_1$, $f(X_2 - X_1) = f(X_2) - f(X_1)$.

Proof. Write $Y_1 = f(X_1)$, etc. Then by Theorem 3.2,

$$f^{-1}(Y_1\,Y_2\,...)\subseteq f^{-1}(Y_1)f^{-1}(Y_2)\,... = X_1X_2\,....$$

Now map both sides of this inequality by the function f into the set $Y = f(X)$. Thus

$$Y_1\,Y_2\,...\subseteq f(X_1X_2\,...)$$

or $$f(X_1)f(X_2)\,...\subseteq f(X_1X_2\,...).$$

From this and Theorem 3.2 the first statement follows. The proof of the second statement is similar.

3.4. THEOREM. *Let $f(x)$ be a bi-uniform function defined in a space X, and A an additive class of subsets $X_1, X_2, ...$ of X. Then also the images $f(X_1), f(X_2), ...$ form an additive class.*
  Proof. Write $Y = f(X)$, $Y_1 = f(X_1)$, etc., and $B = \{Y_1, Y_2, ...\}$. Then:

(i) $$Y = f(X) \in B,$$

since $X \in A$;

(ii) $$Y - Y_1 = f(X) - f(X_1)$$
$$= f(X - X_1) \quad \text{(by Theorem 3.3)}$$
$$\in B,$$

since $X - X_1 \in A$;

(iii) $$Y_1 + Y_2 + ... = f(X_1) + f(X_2) + ...$$
$$= f(X_1 + X_2 + ...) \quad \text{(by Theorem 3.3)}$$
$$\in B,$$

since $X_1 + X_2 + ... \in A$.   Q.E.D.

§ 4. Point sets in the n-dimensional vector space R^n

4.1. DEFINITIONS. A sequence of n real numbers $x_1, x_2, ..., x_n$ is called an *n-dimensional vector*: $x = (x_1, x_2, ..., x_n)$. The numbers x_1, x_2, etc., are said to be the (one-dimensional) *components* of the vector x. A *scalar* is a one-dimensional vector.
  The sum $x + y$ of two vectors

$$x = (x_1, x_2, ..., x_n), \quad y = (y_1, y_2, ..., y_n)$$

is defined by $x + y = (x_1 + y_1, x_2 + y_2, ..., x_n + y_n)$. Their *scalar product*, denoted by xy, $x.y$ or (x,y), is defined by

$$xy = \sum_{\nu=1}^{n} x_\nu y_\nu.$$

If λ is an arbitrary real number, the vector λx is defined by

$$\lambda x = (\lambda x_1, \lambda x_2, ..., \lambda x_n).$$

The set of all n-dimensional vectors is called the n-dimensional number space or *vector space* R^n. An n-dimensional vector x is said to be a *"point"* of R^n and the components $x_1, x_2, ..., x_n$ of x are called the coordinates of the point x.

A k-dimensional *sub-space* R^k of the space R^n, $k < n$, is defined as the set of all k-dimensional vectors $x' = (x'_1, x'_2, ..., x'_k)$ where

$$x'_1 = x_{n_1}, \quad x'_2 = x_{n_2}, ..., \quad x'_k = x_{n_k},$$
$$1 \leqslant n_1 < n_2 < ... < n_k \leqslant n,$$

and $n_1, ..., n_k$ are fixed indices. x' is called a *k-dimensional component* of the n-dimensional vector x. The $(n-k)$-dimensional component of the vector x which is derived from x by omitting all one-dimensional components $x'_1, x'_2, ..., x'_k$ of x', will always be denoted by x/x', and the set of all these vectors x/x' will be called the *complementary sub-space* of R^n and denoted by R^n/R^k.

Let X be a subset of the sub-space R^k of R^n. Then the set of all points x of R^n for which $x' \in X$ is called the *cylinder set* with the base X, and denoted by $X \times (R^n/R^k)$. (As in § 2.2, the symbol $\times$ denotes Cartesian multiplication, with the difference, however, that the original order of components must be preserved in the vectors belonging to the product.)

The *distance* of any two points x, y of R^n is defined as the non-negative number

$$|x-y| \equiv |\sqrt{[(x-y)(x-y)]}|.$$

If a is any point of R^n and ϵ any positive number, then the set of all the points x of R^n for which $|x-a| < \epsilon$ is called the *ϵ-neighbourhood* of a (in R^n).

A subset X of R^n is called an *open set* if, for each point of X, there is a neighbourhood of it which is a subset of X.

A point a of R^n is called a *limiting point* of a subset X of R^n if every neighbourhood of a contains at least one point of X

different from a. (From this it follows immediately that every neighbourhood of a contains an infinite number of points of X.)

A subset X of R^n is called a *closed set* if it contains all its limiting points. A finite set of points (possessing no limiting points at all) is regarded as closed. The empty set is considered as closed and as open at the same time.

The sum of a subset X of R^n and the set of all its limiting points is called the *closure* of X. It is a closed subset of R^n.

Let a be a point of R^n of which every neighbourhood contains at least one point of a subset X of R^n and at least one point of $R^n - X$. Then a is called a *boundary point* of the set X (and of the set $R^n - X$, too).

Let a_ν, b_ν, where $\nu = 1, 2, ..., n$, be $2n$ numbers satisfying the n conditions $a_\nu < b_\nu$, $\nu = 1, 2, ..., n$. Then the set of all the points x of R^n for which $a_\nu < x_\nu < b_\nu$, $\nu = 1, 2, ..., n$, is called an open (finite, or bounded, n-dimensional) *interval* of R^n, and the set of all points x such that $a_\nu \leqslant x_\nu \leqslant b_\nu$ is called, correspondingly, a closed interval. An open interval is an open set, and a closed interval is a closed set. If in the defining inequalities both symbols $<$ and $\leqslant$ occur, the interval is said to be half-open. If, for at least one value of ν, the inequality $a_\nu < b_\nu$ is replaced by the equation $a_\nu = b_\nu$, the corresponding set is called a *degenerate interval*. If, for at least one value of ν, there is no lower or upper bound for the range of admitted values of x_ν, the interval is called infinite or unbounded. If all the differences $b_\nu - a_\nu$ are equal, the interval is called an n-dimensional cube.

A subset X of R^n is said to be *bounded* if it is a subset of a bounded interval.

Let A be any additive class of subsets of R^n which contains all the intervals of R^n. The intersection of all such additive classes is called the aggregate of the *Borel (sub)sets* of R^n. (Thus, it is the "smallest" aggregate containing all intervals.)

4.2. Schwarz' inequality. *For any two n-dimensional vectors x and y,*

$$(xy)(xy) \leqslant (xx)(yy).$$

Proof. Let λ be a (real) parameter. Then, from

$$(x + \lambda y)(x + \lambda y) \geqslant 0$$

for each value of λ, it follows that

$$(xx) + 2\lambda(xy) + \lambda^2 (yy) \geqslant 0.$$

If $y \neq 0$, the statement is obtained by putting $\lambda = -(xy)/(yy)$. If $y = 0$, it is evident.

4.3. Triangular inequality. *For any two n-dimensional vectors x and y,*

$$|x+y| \leqslant |x| + |y|.$$

(See the figure.)

Proof. By Schwarz' inequality 4.2,

$$2xy \leqslant 2|x||y|.$$

Adding
$$xx + yy = |x|^2 + |y|^2$$

yields
$$(x+y)(x+y) \leqslant (|x|+|y|)^2. \qquad \text{Q.E.D.}$$

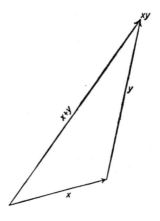

4.4. THEOREM. *The sum of a finite number and the intersection of any number of closed subsets of R^n are closed. The intersection of a finite number and the sum of any number of open subsets of R^n are open.*

Proof. Let $C_1, C_2, ..., C_k$ be k closed subsets of R^n and a a limiting point of their sum $C_1 + C_2 + ... + C_k$. Assume that the statement is wrong, i.e. that a is not a point of $C_1 + ... + C_k$. Hence, $a \in (C_1 + ... + C_k)^* = C_1^* ... C_k^*$ (by Theorem 2.6) and $a \in C_1^*, ..., a \in C_k^*$. On the other hand, a is a limiting point of at least one of the sets $C_1, ..., C_k$ and therefore, by the assumptions of the theorem, an element of this set; say C_1. The contradiction $a \in C_1^*, a \in C_1$ can be made to disappear only by dropping the assumption that $a \notin C_1 + ... + C_k$. This proves the first statement. The proofs of the other statements are similar.

Note. That the intersection of an infinite number of open sets need not be open is shown by the following infinite sequence of sets

$$-\frac{1}{\nu} < x < +\frac{1}{\nu}, \quad \nu = 1, 2, 3, \dots .$$

Correspondingly, the sum of an infinite number of closed sets need not be closed. (Cf. Corollary II of Theorem 4.8.)

4.5. THEOREM. *For each positive number ϵ, there is an enumerable aggregate of ϵ-neighbourhoods in R^n such that any subset of R^n is contained in (or "covered by") the sum of a finite or enumerable number of these neighbourhoods suitably chosen.*

Proof. By means of a "network" similar to that shown in the figure, the whole space can be represented as the sum of an enumerable number of closed cubes having edges of length δ. Choose $\delta < 2\epsilon/\sqrt{n}$. Then any cube lies in the interior of a sphere of radius ϵ around the centre of this cube. Hence, each point of R^n belongs to at least one of these ϵ-neighbourhoods, and this proves the statement.

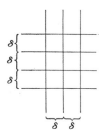

4.6. HEINE–BOREL THEOREM. *Suppose that a neighbourhood corresponds to each point of a bounded closed subset C of R^n. Then the set C is covered by the sum of a finite number of these neighbourhoods.*

Proof. Certainly C is covered by the sum of an infinite number of neighbourhoods. Suppose that, in fact, an infinite number is needed for the covering of C. Now, by the assumptions of the theorem, C is a subset of a closed cube C_0 having edges of length s, say. Represent C_0 as the sum of 2^n closed cubes having edges of length $s/2$ by halving the intervals $a_\nu \dots b_\nu$ which define C_0 (cf. the figure overleaf). At least one of these 2^n sub-cubes needs an infinite number of neighbourhoods in order to be covered. Choose one of them and call it C_1. In the same way, derive a sub-cube C_2 of C_1 with the edge length $s/2^2$, etc. The sequence of cubes $C_0, C_1, C_2, \ldots$, each of which lies in its predecessor, converges towards a point a of C. Let A be the neighbourhood corresponding to a which has the radius ϵ. For $s/2^k < \epsilon/\sqrt{n}$, all cubes $C_k, C_{k+1}, C_{k+2}, \ldots$ are subsets of A. In particular, $C_k \subseteq A$, whereas by the assumption of the proof, C_k needs an infinite number of neighbourhoods in order to be covered. Hence this assumption is wrong; i.e. the statement of the theorem is true.

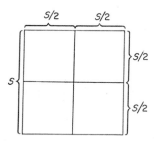

4.7. THEOREM. *Any (non-empty) open subset of R^n can be represented as a sum of an enumerable number of closed intervals.*

Proof. Cover the whole space R^n by a network of closed cubes with edge lengths δ. Certain cubes $C_1, C_2, \ldots$ are subsets of the given open set O. Divide each cube of this network into 2^n component sub-cubes by means of a second similar network, so that its cubes have edges of the length $\delta/2$. Then there are cubes C_1', C_2' of this finer network such that

$$C_1' \subseteq O - (C_1 + C_2 + \ldots),$$

$$C_2' \subseteq O - (C_1 + C_2 + \ldots),$$

etc. Hence

$$O \supseteq (C_1 + C_2 + \ldots) + (C_1' + C_2' + \ldots) + \ldots .$$

Conversely, each point of O belongs to at least one of the cubes constructed in this way. Hence

$$O \subseteq (C_1 + C_2 + \ldots) + (C_1' + C_2' + \ldots) + \ldots,$$

and this, with the preceding inequality, proves the statement.

COROLLARY. *Open sets are Borel sets.*

4.8. THEOREM. *The complement of a closed subset of R^n is open, and the complement of an open set is closed.*

Proof. Let C be a closed subset of R^n and a a point of $R^n - C$. If there were no neighbourhood of a as a subset of $R^n - C$, then there would be points of C different from a in every neighbourhood of a, i.e. a would be a limiting point of C, which contradicts the assumptions that C is closed and $a \in R^n - C$. Hence there is at least one neighbourhood of a which is a subset of $R^n - C$, and this is the first statement of the theorem. The proof of the second statement is similar.

Note. Like the empty set, the whole space R^n (its complement) is open and closed at the same time.

COROLLARY I. *Closed sets are Borel sets* (cf. Corollary 4.7).

COROLLARY II. An open set can be represented as the sum of an enumerable number of closed sets (see Theorem 4.7). Conversely, a closed set can be represented as the intersection of an enumerable number of open sets.

For, if the letters C and O always denote closed and open sets, respectively, and asterisks denote complements, then

$$C = O^*$$

$$= \left(\sum_{\nu=1}^{\infty} C_\nu \right)^*$$

$$= \prod_{\nu=1}^{\infty} C_\nu^* \qquad \text{(by Theorem 2.6)}$$

$$= \prod_{\nu=1}^{\infty} O_\nu.$$

4.9. THEOREM. *Let R^k be a sub-space of R^n and B a Borel subset of R^k. Then the cylinder set $B \times (R^n/R^k)$ is a Borel subset of R^n.*

Proof. For an interval J of R^k the statement is evident. Since there is a one-to-one correspondence between the Borel subsets B of R^k and the subsets $B \times (R^n/R^k)$ of R^n, the aggregate of all these sets is the smallest additive class of subsets of R^n which contains all the infinite intervals $J \times (R^n/R^k)$. Hence all the sets $B \times (R^n/R^k)$ are Borel subsets of R^n.

§ 5. Topological mapping in vector spaces

5.1. DEFINITIONS. Let $f(x)$ be a function defined in a subset X of the vector space R^n which maps X into a subset Y of the vector space R^p. It is said to be *continuous* in the point a of X if for each ϵ-neighbourhood $V_\epsilon(b)$ of $b = f(a)$ in R^p there is a δ neighbourhood $U_\delta(a)$ of a in R^n such that

$$f\{XU_\delta(a)\} \subseteq V_\epsilon(b);$$

i.e. if

$$|f(x) - f(a)|_{(p)} < \epsilon \quad \text{for} \quad |x - a|_{(n)} < \delta = \delta(\epsilon), \quad x \in X.$$

The function $f(x)$ is said to be continuous in the set X if it is continuous in each point of X. It is called *uniformly continuous* in X if, for every positive value of ϵ, a positive value of δ can be found which depends only on ϵ, and does not depend on the particular point a of X.

Let a function $f(x)$ which is defined, bi-uniform and continuous in the set X, possess an inverse function f^{-1} which is continuous in the set $Y = f(X)$. Then the mapping of the set X on the set Y is said to be *topological*.

5.2. THEOREM. *Any function $f(x)$ which is defined and continuous in a bounded closed subset C of R^n is uniformly continuous in C.*

Proof. For any fixed positive value of ϵ, there is, for each point x of C, a neighbourhood $|x' - x| < \delta(x)$ of x such that $|f(x') - f(x)| < \frac{1}{2}\epsilon$. By the Heine–Borel Theorem (4.6) the set C is covered by the sum of a finite number of neighbourhoods $|x' - x_\lambda| < \frac{1}{2}\delta(x_\lambda)$, $\lambda = 1, 2, ..., l$, say. Now let δ_0 be any positive number $\leqslant \frac{1}{2} \min\limits_{1 \leqslant \lambda \leqslant l} \delta(x_\lambda)$. Then, for any two points $x^{(1)}, x^{(2)}$ of C having a distance $< \delta_0$,

$$|f(x^{(2)}) - f(x^{(1)})| < \epsilon.$$

For, there is a point x_λ such that

$$|x^{(1)} - x_\lambda| < \frac{1}{2}\delta(x_\lambda);$$

therefore

$$|f(x^{(1)}) - f(x_\lambda)| < \frac{1}{2}\epsilon.$$

Further,

$$|x^{(2)} - x_\lambda| \leqslant |x^{(2)} - x^{(1)}| + |x^{(1)} - x_\lambda| \qquad \text{(by 4.3)}$$

$$< \delta_0 + \frac{1}{2}\delta(x_\lambda)$$

$$\leqslant \delta(x_\lambda).$$

Hence, $\qquad |f(x^{(2)}) - f(x_\lambda)| < \tfrac{1}{2}\epsilon,$

and $\qquad |f(x^{(2)}) - f(x^{(1)})| \leqslant |f(x^{(2)}) - f(x_\lambda)|$

$$+ |f(x_\lambda) - f(x^{(1)})|$$

$$< \tfrac{1}{2}\epsilon + \tfrac{1}{2}\epsilon. \qquad \text{Q.E.D.}$$

5.3. THEOREM. *Let $f(x)$ be a function which maps R^n continuously into R^1, and let c be any constant. Then the set of all the points x of R^n for which $f(x) < c$ is open. The sets for which $f(x) \leqslant c$ or $f(x) = c$ are closed.*

Proof. If $f(x_0) < c$, then $f(x) < f(x_0) + \epsilon$ for $|x - x_0| < \delta(\epsilon)$. Choose $\epsilon \leqslant c - f(x_0)$. Then $f(x) < f(x_0) + \{c - f(x_0)\} = c$ if $|x - x_0| < \delta(\epsilon)$. Hence, the set of all the points x of R^n for which $f(x) < c$ is open. The other proofs are similar.

5.4. THEOREM. *Let $f(x)$ and $g(x)$ be two topological mappings of the vector space R^n on itself. Then $g[f(x)]$ is also a topological mapping of R^n on itself.*

Proof. The bi-uniformity of $g[f(x)]$ is evident. Its continuity follows from

$$|f(x) - f(a)| < \epsilon \quad \text{for} \quad |x - a| < \delta(\epsilon)$$

and $\qquad |g(y) - g(b)| < \eta \quad \text{for} \quad |y - b| < \zeta(\eta)$

that $\qquad |g\{f(x)\} - g\{f(a)\}| < \eta$

for $|f(x) - f(a)| < \zeta(\eta)$ and so much more for $|x - a| < \delta\{\zeta(\eta)\}$.

The proof that the inverse mapping $f^{-1}g^{-1}$ is continuous is similar.

5.5. THEOREM. *For a topological mapping of the space R^n on itself, the image of a proper subset of R^n is a proper subset of R^n. Similarly, the image of a bounded, or open, or closed, or Borel subset of R^n is a bounded, open, closed, or Borel subset of R^n, respectively.*

Proofs will be given for open and for Borel subsets only. The proofs of the other statements are similar to the proof for open sets.

Suppose the topological image $f(O)$ of the open set O is not open. Then there is at least one point b of $f(O)$ such that each of its neighbourhoods contains at least one point of

$R^n - f(O)$. Let $a = f^{-1}(b)$ and $U_\epsilon(a)$ be a neighbourhood of a which is a subset of O. Then, for the continuity of f^{-1}, there is a neighbourhood $U_\delta(b)$ of b such that

$$f^{-1}\{U_\delta(b)\} \subseteq U_\epsilon(a).$$

Further, let d be a point of $U_\delta(b)$ not belonging to $f(O)$. Then $c = f^{-1}(d)$ is a point in $U_\epsilon(a)$ and, therefore, in O. So $d = f(c)$ lies in $f(O)$—which contradicts the assumption just made that $d \notin f(O)$. Hence there is no point b of the required kind, i.e. $f(O)$ is open.

The Borel subsets B of R^n form an additive class. Hence, also, the images $f(B)$ form an additive class (by Theorem 3.4). It contains all open and all closed intervals since their originals are open or closed and, therefore, Borel sets. Therefore the aggregate of all sets $f(B)$ contains all Borel sets

$$\{f(B_1), f(B_2), \ldots\} \supseteq \{B_1, B_2, \ldots\}.$$

The same argument applies to the topological mapping f^{-1} of R^n on itself. Hence

$$\{f^{-1}(B_1), f^{-1}(B_2), \ldots\} \supseteq \{B_1, B_2, \ldots\}$$

or, by the operation f on both sides,

$$\{B_1, B_2, \ldots\} \supseteq \{f(B_1), f(B_2), \ldots\},$$

so that finally,

$$\{B_1, B_2, \ldots\} \supseteq \{f(B_1), f(B_2), \ldots\} \supseteq \{B_1, B_2, \ldots\}.$$

Q.E.D.

§ 6. Systems of ordinary differential equations

In statistical mechanics, the topological mapping of a vector space R^n on to itself is always generated by "equations of motion", i.e. by systems of ordinary differential equations (cf. § 1). Therefore we shall now collect the basic theorems about such equations.

The following assumptions are made in all the propositions of this section.

6.1. GENERAL ASSUMPTIONS. In the $(n+1)$-dimensional vector space R^{n+1} of the variable $(x, t) = (x_1, x_2, \ldots, x_n, t)$, there are n scalar functions $X_i(x, t)$, $i = 1, \ldots, n$, defined which depend on (x, t) continuously. For each closed interval J of R^{n+1} given by

$$\left.\begin{array}{ll} |x_i - \overset{0}{x}_i| \leqslant c, & i = 1, 2, \ldots, n, \\ |t - \overset{0}{t}| \leqslant |t^1 - \overset{0}{t}| & \end{array}\right\}$$

(where $c > 0$, $\overset{0}{t}$ and t^1 are any constants), there is a "Lipschitz constant" N_J, i.e. a positive constant N_J such that

$$|X_i(x', t) - X_i(x, t)| \leqslant N_J \sum_{j=1}^{n} |x'_j - x_j|, \quad i = 1, 2, \ldots, n,$$

for each $(x, t) \in J$, $(x', t) \in J$.

Note. In the following proofs there are slight and obvious differences in the cases $t^1 > \overset{0}{t}$ and $t^1 < \overset{0}{t}$. (The case $t^1 = \overset{0}{t}$ is trivial.) We shall deal only with the case $t^1 > \overset{0}{t}$ which, in the applications, is more important.

6.2. EXISTENCE AND UNIQUENESS THEOREM. *Under the assumptions* 6.1 *the system of ordinary differential equations*

$$\frac{\mathrm{d}x_i}{\mathrm{d}t} = X_i(x, t), \quad i = 1, 2, \ldots, n,$$

possesses, in the time interval,

$$\overset{0}{t} \leqslant t \leqslant t_1 \equiv \min\left(t^1, \overset{0}{t} + \frac{c}{M}\right),$$

exactly one solution $x_i = \chi_i(\overset{0}{x}, \overset{0}{t}, t)$ *which satisfies the initial condition*

$$\chi_i(\overset{0}{x}, \overset{0}{t}, \overset{0}{t}) = \overset{0}{x}_i, \quad i = 1, 2, \ldots, n$$

for arbitrarily chosen values of $\overset{0}{x}, \overset{0}{t}$. *Here* M *denotes a common upper bound of the functions* $|X_i(x, t)|$ *in the interval* J. *Let the sequences of functions* $\chi_i^{(0)}(\overset{0}{x}, \overset{0}{t}, t), \chi_i^{(1)}(\overset{0}{x}, \overset{0}{t}, t), \chi_i^{(2)}(\overset{0}{x}, \overset{0}{t}, t), \ldots$, *where* $i = 1, 2, \ldots, n$, *be defined by the iterative scheme*

$$\chi_i^{(0)} \equiv \overset{0}{x}_i, \quad \chi_i^{(\nu+1)} \equiv \overset{0}{x}_i + \int_{t^0}^{t} X_i\{\chi^{(\nu)}(\overset{0}{x}, \overset{0}{t}, \tau), \tau\} \, \mathrm{d}\tau,$$

$$\nu = 0, 1, 2, \ldots, \quad i = 1, 2, \ldots, n.$$

Then the functions $\chi_i^{(\nu)}(\overset{0}{x}, \overset{0}{t}, t)$ *tend uniformly towards the solution functions* $\chi_i(\overset{0}{x}, \overset{0}{t}, t)$ *for all moments* t *of the closed time interval* $\overset{0}{t} \ldots t_1$, *if* $\nu \to \infty$.

Outline of the proof. Let J' be the $(n+1)$-dimensional interval

$$|x_i - \overset{o}{x}_i| \leqslant c, \quad i = 1, 2, \ldots, n, \\ \overset{o}{t} \leqslant t \leqslant t_1.$$

From the iterative scheme it follows by induction that $[\chi^{(\nu)}(\overset{o}{x}, \overset{o}{t}, t), t] \in J'$, if $\overset{o}{t} \leqslant t \leqslant t_1$. Further, for the same values of t, it follows from $|\chi_i^{(1)} - \overset{o}{x}_i| \leqslant M . (t - \overset{o}{t})$, $i = 1, \ldots, n$, the iterative scheme and the Lipschitz condition, that

$$|\chi_i^{(2)} - \chi_i^{(1)}| \leqslant N_J \sum_{j=1}^{n} \int_{t^o}^{t} |\chi_j^{(1)} - \chi_j^{(0)}| \, d\tau \leqslant \frac{1}{2!} MnN_J(t - \overset{o}{t})^2,$$

$$|\chi_i^{(3)} - \chi_i^{(2)}| \leqslant \frac{1}{3!} M(nN_J)^2 (t - \overset{o}{t})^3,$$

etc. Therefore the n series

$$\overset{o}{x}_i + \sum_{\nu=0}^{\infty} (\chi_i^{(\nu+1)} - \chi_i^{(\nu)}), \quad i = 1, 2, \ldots, n$$

converge towards limits $\chi_i(\overset{o}{x}, \overset{o}{t}, t)$. Since the convergence is uniform in J' and since all the terms are continuous functions of t (proof by induction), these limits are continuous functions of t, too. Now

$$\left| \chi_i - \overset{o}{x}_i - \int_{t^o}^{t} X_i(\chi, \tau) \, d\tau \right|$$

$$= \left| \left\{ \chi_i - \overset{o}{x}_i - \int_{t^o}^{t} X_i(\chi, \tau) \, d\tau \right\} - \right.$$

$$\left. - \left\{ \chi_i^{(\nu+1)} - \overset{o}{x}_i - \int_{t^o}^{t} X_i(\chi^\nu, \tau) \, d\tau \right\} \right|$$

$$\leqslant |\chi_i - \chi_i^{(\nu+1)}| + \int_{t^o}^{t} |X_i(\chi^\nu, \tau) - X_i(\chi, \tau)| \, d\tau.$$

The right-hand side tends towards 0 if $\nu \to \infty$. Hence the left-hand side vanishes identically, and by differentiation with respect to t, the (vector) function $\chi(\overset{o}{x}, \overset{o}{t}, t)$ is shown to be a solution of the given system of differential equations.

The uniqueness of the solution is proved similarly. Suppose that there is a second solution $\bar{\chi}$. By means of the iterative scheme, the differences $|\chi_i^{(\nu)} - \bar{\chi}_i|$ are estimated and shown to tend towards zero if $\nu \to \infty$. Hence, $\chi \equiv \bar{\chi}$.   Q.E.D.

Note. All this has been shown for the interval $\overset{\circ}{t} \leqslant t \leqslant t_1$. The solution cannot always be continued up to indefinitely large values of t as is shown by the following example,

$$\frac{dx}{dt} = x^{1+\eta}$$

where $x \in R^1$ and η is a positive constant. Its solution with the initial condition $x = \overset{\circ}{x} > 0$ for $t = 0$ reads:

$$x = \overset{\circ}{x}(1 - \eta \overset{\circ}{x}{}^\eta t)^{-1/\eta}.$$

For $t \to 1/\eta \overset{\circ}{x}{}^\eta$, it tends towards infinity.

The following theorem gives a sufficient condition for the indefinite extension of the solution.

6.3. THEOREM. *Suppose that the assumptions 6.1 are valid and, further, that there is a Lipschitz constant N common to all intervals J of R^{n+1}. Then the solution $\chi(\overset{\circ}{x}, \overset{\circ}{t}, t)$ of the system of differential equations $\dot{x} = X(x, t)$ (as given by Theorem 6.2) can be uniquely extended to indefinitely large values of t.*

Proof. Extend the solution $\chi(\overset{\circ}{x}, \overset{\circ}{t}, t)$ defined in $\overset{\circ}{t} \leqslant t \leqslant t_1$ by starting from the initial value $x^1 = \chi(\overset{\circ}{x}, \overset{\circ}{t}, t_1)$ for $t = t_1$. By Theorem 6.2, this is feasible up to a moment $t_2 > t_1$, etc. Thus a strictly monotonic increasing sequence $t_1, t_2, t_3, \ldots$ is obtained. Suppose that there are moments t which cannot be reached in this way (see Note, 6.2), and let t^* be their lower limit. Obviously, t^* belongs to them (for, otherwise, $x^* = \chi(\overset{\circ}{x}, \overset{\circ}{t}, t^*)$ would be defined and the solution $(\overset{\circ}{x}, \overset{\circ}{t}, t)$ could be extended beyond the instant t^* by starting from the initial values x^*, t^*). Now from the Lipschitz condition it follows that

$$|X_i(x, t)| \leqslant |X_i(0, t)| + N \sum_{j=1}^{n} |x_j|$$

for all (x, t) and

$$|X_i(x, t)| \leqslant C + N \sum_{j=1}^{n} |x_j|, \quad C = \text{const.} > 0,$$

for all x and $0 \leqslant t \leqslant t^*$. By means of mathematical induction with respect to ν and the iterative scheme, it is shown that

$$|\chi_i^{(\nu)}| \leqslant |\overset{\circ}{x}_i| + \frac{1}{n}(e^{nN(t-t^0)} - 1)\left(\sum_{j=1}^{n} |x_j| + \frac{C}{N}\right)$$

for $0 \leqslant t < t^*$. Hence the solution functions $\chi_i(\overset{\circ}{x}, \overset{\circ}{l}, t)$ are bounded in the half-open interval $\overset{\circ}{l} \leqslant t < t^*$, and so are the functions $X_i\{\chi(\overset{\circ}{x}, \overset{\circ}{l}, t), t\}$, say, by the constant M^*. Now $t_\nu \to t^*$, and by the Mean-Value Theorem of differential calculus,

$$|\chi_i(\overset{\circ}{x}, \overset{\circ}{l}, t_{l+p}) - \chi_i(\overset{\circ}{x}, \overset{\circ}{l}, t_l)| \leqslant |t_{l+p} - t_l| \cdot \sup_{t_l \leqslant t \leqslant t_{l+p}} \left| \frac{\mathrm{d}x_i}{\mathrm{d}t} \right|$$

$$= |t_{l+p} - t_l| \cdot \sup_{t_l \leqslant t \leqslant t_{l+p}} |X_i(x, t)| \leqslant |t_{l+p} - t_l| \, M^*.$$

Hence, by Cauchy's convergence criterion, $\chi_i(\overset{\circ}{x}, \overset{\circ}{l}, t_\nu)$ converges towards a limit $x_i^* = \chi(\overset{\circ}{x}, \overset{\circ}{l}, t^*)$ if $\nu \to \infty$. On account of the continuity, $\chi_i(\overset{\circ}{x}, \overset{\circ}{l}, t)$ also converges if $t \to t^*$ and $t < t^*$. Since $\dot{\chi}_i(\overset{\circ}{x}, \overset{\circ}{l}, t) = X_i\{\chi(\overset{\circ}{x}, \overset{\circ}{l}, t), t\}$ if $\overset{\circ}{l} \leqslant t < t^*$, there are also limits for the derivatives $\dot{\chi}_i$, which, together with x^*, t^*, satisfy the differential equations. So the solution $\chi(\overset{\circ}{x}, \overset{\circ}{l}, t)$ can be extended to the moment t^*, hence, as shown before, beyond t^*—which contradicts the definition of t^*. This contradiction disappears only if there is no such instant t^*.   Q.E.D.

6.4. THEOREM. *Under the assumptions* 6.1, *the solution* $\chi(\overset{\circ}{x}, \overset{\circ}{l}, t)$ *of the system of differential equations* $\dot{x} = X(x, t)$ *depends, for any moment* t *of the time interval* $\overset{\circ}{l} \leqslant t < t_1$, *continuously on the initial point* $\overset{\circ}{x}$.

Outline of the proof. Let t_1' be a moment of the open interval $\overset{\circ}{l} \ldots t_1$, $\overset{\circ}{x}$ be a fixed starting point and ξ a variable starting point in the neighbourhood $|\xi - \overset{\circ}{x}| < \delta$, the radius δ of which is restricted by the conditions that $\delta < M \cdot (t_1 - t_1')$ and $\delta \leqslant c$. Then, in the interval $\overset{\circ}{l} \leqslant t \leqslant t_1'$, the sequences of functions

$$\chi_i^{(0)}(\xi, \overset{\circ}{l}, t), \quad \chi_i^{(1)}(\xi, \overset{\circ}{l}, t), \; \ldots,$$

which all depend continuously on ξ (proof by induction), converge uniformly towards the solution functions $\chi_i(\xi, \overset{\circ}{l}, t)$. Hence these depend continuously on ξ. (For details of this and the next proof, cf. Kamke's book.)

6.5. THEOREM. *Suppose that the functions* $X_i(x, t)$, $i = 1, 2, \ldots, n$ *satisfy the assumptions* 6.1. *Further, let them depend on a finite number of parameters* $p_1, p_2, \ldots$ *in such a fashion that they are continuous functions of* (x, t, p) *in the set of points* (x, t, p) *in which they are defined. Here* p *denotes the vector* $(p_1, p_2, \ldots)$.

Then the solution $\chi(\overset{0}{x}, \overset{0}{t}, t, p)$ *of the system of differential equations* $\dot{x} = X(x, t, p)$ *depends on* p *continuously.*

The proof is based on successive approximations in the same way as the proof 6.4.

6.6. THEOREM. *Suppose that the functions* $X_i(x, t)$, $i = 1, 2, ..., n$ *satisfy the assumptions* 6.1 *and, further, that they possess partial derivatives* $X_{ij}(x, t) \equiv (\partial/\partial x_j) X_i(x, t)$, $j = 1, ..., n$, *in the interval* J *which are continuous functions of* (x, t). *Then the solution functions* $\chi_i(\overset{0}{x}, \overset{0}{t}, t)$ *possess derivatives*

$$\left. \begin{array}{l} \chi_{ij}(\overset{0}{x}, \overset{0}{t}, t) \equiv \dfrac{\partial}{\partial \overset{0}{x}_j} \chi_i(\overset{0}{x}, \overset{0}{t}, t), \\[3mm] \chi_{i0}(\overset{0}{x}, \overset{0}{t}, t) \equiv \dfrac{\partial}{\partial \overset{0}{t}} \chi_i(\overset{0}{x}, \overset{0}{t}, t), \end{array} \right\} \quad i, j = 1, 2, ..., n,$$

everywhere in R^{n+2} *where they are defined. These derivatives are continuous functions of* $\overset{0}{x}$, $\overset{0}{t}$ *and* t, *and are the uniquely determined solutions of both of the systems of differential equations*

$$\dot{\chi}_{ik} = \sum_{j=1}^{n} X_{ij}\{\chi(\overset{0}{x}, \overset{0}{t}, t), t\} \chi_{jk}, \quad i, k = 1, 2, ..., n,$$

and $\quad \dot{\chi}_{i0} = \sum_{j=1}^{n} X_{ij}\{\chi(\overset{0}{x}, \overset{0}{t}, t), t\} \chi_{i0}, \quad i = 1, 2, ..., n,$

with the initial conditions

$$\chi_{ik}(\overset{0}{x}, \overset{0}{t}, \overset{0}{t}) = \delta_{ik} \equiv \begin{cases} 1 \text{ if } i = k, \\ 0 \text{ if } i \neq k, \end{cases}$$

and $\qquad \chi_{i0}(\overset{0}{x}, \overset{0}{t}, \overset{0}{t}) = - X_i(\overset{0}{x}, \overset{0}{t}).$

Outline of the proof. Let $\overset{0}{x}$ be a fixed and ξ a variable initial point in a neighbourhood of $\overset{0}{x}$. Then, by the Mean-Value Theorem of differential calculus,

$$\frac{\dot{\chi}_i(\xi, \overset{0}{t}, t) - \dot{\chi}_i(\overset{0}{x}, \overset{0}{t}, t)}{\xi_k - \overset{0}{x}_k} = \frac{X_i\{\chi(\xi, \overset{0}{t}, t), t\} - X_i\{\chi(\overset{0}{x}, \overset{0}{t}, t), t\}}{\xi_k - \overset{0}{x}_k}$$

$$= \sum_{j=1}^{n} \{X_{ij}[\chi(\overset{0}{x}, \overset{0}{t}, t), t] + \epsilon_{ij}\} \frac{\chi_j(\xi, \overset{0}{t}, t) - \chi_j(\overset{0}{x}, \overset{0}{t}, t)}{\xi_k - \overset{0}{x}_k}$$

where the functions $\epsilon_{ij} \equiv \epsilon_{ij}(\overset{0}{x}, \xi, \overset{0}{t}, t) \to 0$ if $|\xi - \overset{0}{x}| \to 0$. According to Theorem 6.5, the solutions of this system of differential equations and of that in the theorem for χ_{ik} differ arbitrarily little if $|\xi - \overset{0}{x}|$ is sufficiently small, and if the initial conditions are equal.

COROLLARY. If the functions $X_i(x,t)$ possess continuous derivatives of kth order with respect to $x_1, x_2, \ldots, x_n$, the solution function $\chi_i(\overset{0}{x}, \overset{0}{t}, t)$ possesses continuous derivatives of kth order with respect to $\overset{0}{x}_1, \ldots, \overset{0}{x}_n$.

The proof follows from the theorem by induction.

§ 7. The Lebesgue measure

In statistical mechanics, often the "volumes" or "measures" of point sets have to be considered. The usual concept of measure attributed to Riemann or Peano is, however, not suitable: not every "reasonable" point set need possess a Riemann measure and, in particular, the topological image of a set which is Riemann-measurable need not be Riemann-measurable itself. But it is just this property (that the topological image of a measurable set be measurable) that is an indispensable requirement for statistical mechanics. Hence we have to look for a concept of measure which satisfies this requirement for a sufficiently general class of sets. Such a class is that of the Borel sets, and the concept of measure which is to be applied is that of Lebesgue.

7.1. DEFINITIONS. The n-dimensional measure μJ of a bounded n-dimensional open interval J given by

$$a_\nu < x_\nu < b_\nu, \quad \nu = 1, 2, \ldots, n$$

is defined by
$$\mu J = \prod_{\nu=1}^{n} (b_\nu - a_\nu).$$

Let S be any subset of R^n and $\{J_1, J_2, \ldots\}$ a finite or enumerable aggregate of bounded n-dimensional open intervals the sum of which covers S so that

$$S \subseteq J_1 + J_2 + \ldots .$$

To each aggregate of this kind there corresponds a number

$$\mu S_1 + \mu S_2 + \ldots$$

(including ∞). The lower limit of all these numbers is called *the outer measure* of the set S and is denoted by $\bar\mu S$. Immediate consequences of this definition are the inequalities

$$\bar{\mu}(S_1 + S_2 + \ldots) \leqslant \bar{\mu}S_1 + \bar{\mu}S_2 + \ldots$$

and $\bar{\mu}S_1 \leqslant \bar{\mu}S_2$ if $S_1 \leqslant S_2$.

Let S be a subset of a bounded open interval J. Then the *inner measure* $\underline{\mu}S$ of the set S is defined by

$$\underline{\mu}S = \mu J - \bar{\mu}(J - S).$$

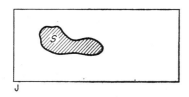

It seems evident and can easily be proved that $\underline{\mu}S$ is independent of the particular choice of J. Further, from the inequality

$$\mu J = \bar{\mu}J \leqslant \bar{\mu}S + \bar{\mu}(J - S)$$

and the definition of the inner measure, it follows that

$$\underline{\mu}S \leqslant \bar{\mu}S.$$

A bounded subset S of R^n is called Lebesgue-measurable or a *Lebesgue set* if $\underline{\mu}S = \bar{\mu}S$. The common value of its outer and inner measures is named its (Lebesgue) measure and denoted by μS. An unbounded subset S of R^n is said to be Lebesgue-measurable if its intersections with all open bounded intervals J are measurable. Its measure μS is defined as the upper limit (which may be finite or infinite) of all the numbers $\mu(S.J)$.

7.2. THEOREMS. The open subsets of R^n are Lebesgue-measurable.

The outer measure of a bounded set S equals the lower limit of the measure of all open sets O which cover S; i.e.

$$\bar{\mu}S = \inf_{S \subseteq O} \mu O.$$

For any two open sets O_1 and O_2,

$$\mu(O_1 + O_2) + \mu(O_1 O_2) = \mu O_1 + \mu O_2.$$

For any two bounded subsets S_1, S_2 of R^n,

$$\left.\begin{aligned}\bar{\mu}(S_1 + S_2) + \bar{\mu}(S_1 S_2) &\leqslant \bar{\mu}S_1 + \bar{\mu}S_2, \\ \underline{\mu}(S_1 + S_2) + \underline{\mu}(S_1 S_2) &\geqslant \underline{\mu}S_1 + \underline{\mu}S_2.\end{aligned}\right\}$$

Proofs. The statements about open sets follow from the definitions and the theorems 4.7 and 4.4. The last inequality is obtained by the application of the last but one inequality to the sets $J - S_1, J - S_2$ where J denotes an interval containing both S_1 and S_2. The last but one inequality is derived from the corresponding equation for open sets and the representation of $\bar{\mu}S$ by means of open sets: for any positive number ϵ there are open sets O_1 and O_2 such that

$$\left.\begin{aligned}S_1 &\subseteq O_1, \\ \bar{\mu}S_1 &\leqslant \mu O_1 < \bar{\mu}S_1 + \epsilon,\end{aligned}\right\}$$

$$\left.\begin{aligned}S_2 &\subseteq O_2, \\ \bar{\mu}S_2 &\leqslant \mu O_2 < \bar{\mu}S_2 + \epsilon.\end{aligned}\right\}$$

Hence

$$\bar{\mu}(S_1 + S_2) + \bar{\mu}(S_1 S_2) \leqslant \mu(O_1 + O_2) + \mu(O_1 O_2)$$

$$= \mu O_1 + \mu O_2 < \bar{\mu}S_1 + \bar{\mu}S_2 + 2\epsilon,$$

or

$$\bar{\mu}(S_1 + S_2) + \bar{\mu}(S_1 S_2) \leqslant \bar{\mu}S_1 + \bar{\mu}S_2.$$

Q.E.D.

7.3. THEOREM. *Let* $\{S_1, S_2, \ldots\}$ *be a finite or enumerable aggregate of measurable sets. Then their sum and their intersection are measurable, too. If the intersections of any two sets are empty, then*

$$\mu(S_1 + S_2 + \ldots) = \mu S_1 + \mu S_2 + \ldots.$$

The difference of two measurable sets S_1 *and* $S_2 \supseteq S_1$ *is measurable and*

$$\mu(S_2 - S_1) = \mu S_2 - \mu S_1.$$

Proof. For two measurable sets S_1 and S_2,

$$\bar{\mu}(S_1 + S_2) + \bar{\mu}(S_1 S_2) \leqslant \bar{\mu}S_1 + \bar{\mu}S_2 \qquad \text{(by 7.2)}$$

$$= \mu S_1 + \mu S_2$$

$$= \underline{\mu}S_1 + \underline{\mu}S_2$$

$$\leqslant \underline{\mu}(S_1 + S_2) + \underline{\mu}(S_1 S_2), \qquad \text{(by 7.2)}$$

hence, by 7.1,

$$\bar{\mu}(S_1 + S_2) = \underline{\mu}(S_1 + S_2),$$
$$\bar{\mu}(S_1 S_2) = \underline{\mu}(S_1 S_2).$$

The proof for any finite number of sets is similar, and it is so if there is an enumerable aggregate of sets all mutual intersections of which are empty. If there are non-empty intersections, put

$$S_1' = S_1,$$
$$S_2' = S_1 + S_2,$$
$$S_3' = S_1 + S_2 + S_3,$$
$$\text{-----------.}$$

Then $\quad S_1 + S_2 + \ldots = S_1' + (S_2' - S_1') + (S_3' - S_2') + \ldots$

Now the terms on the right-hand side have only empty intersections. The statement about subtraction follows immediately from that about addition, and the statement about intersection follows from Theorem 2.6, which states that

$$S_1 S_2 \ldots = R^n - (S_1^* + S_2^* + \ldots)$$

where $S_1^* = R^n - S_1$, etc.

7.4. THEOREM. *The aggregate of all Lebesgue subsets of R^n is an additive class which contains all Borel subsets of R^n.*

Proof. By §§ 2.2 and 7.3, the measurable sets form an additive class; by Definition 7.1 it contains all intervals; by Theorem 4.10 it contains, therefore, all Borel sets.

Note. Not all the subsets of R^n are Lebesgue-measurable, and, in particular, the topological image of a Lebesgue set need not be a Lebesgue set as well. (Cf., however, Theorem 11.2.) But the topological image of a Borel set is Lebesgue-measurable since, by Theorem 5.4, it is itself a Borel set. The importance of the Borel sets in statistical mechanics is based on their three properties of additivity, topological invariance and measurability. The following theorem shows that the use of Borel sets instead of Lebesgue sets does not involve an essential restriction.

7.5. THEOREM. *For any Lebesgue set L there are always two Borel sets A and B such that*

$$A \subseteq L \subseteq B \quad and \quad \mu A = \mu L = \mu B.$$

In other words, for each Lebesgue set there are Borel sets which differ from it only by sets of measure zero.

Proof. Let O be an open set which covers L. Since

$$\mu L = \bar{\mu}L = \inf_{O \supseteq L} \mu O,$$

there is an infinite sequence of open sets $O_1, O_2, \ldots$ such that

$$O_\nu \supseteq L \quad and \quad \lim_{\nu \to \infty} \mu O_\nu = \mu L.$$

Now

$$\mu L \leqslant \mu(O_1 O_2 \ldots O_\nu)$$

$$\leqslant \mu O_\nu;$$

hence

$$\lim_{\nu \to \infty} \mu(O_1 \ldots O_\nu)$$

exists and equals μL. The set $B = O_1 O_2 \ldots$ is, by Theorem 2.7, a Borel set. The proof of the existence of the set A is similar.

7.6. If the set S is covered only by the sums of finite aggregates of open (or, more usually, closed) intervals, instead of by that of a finite or enumerable aggregate, the corresponding concepts of Riemann's (or Peano's) theory of measure are obtained. Now, in this case, the aggregate of all sets admitted to cover S is a sub-aggregate of all the sets admitted in the case of Lebesgue's measure. Hence

$$\bar{\mu}_{\text{Riemann}} \geqslant \bar{\mu}_{\text{Lebesgue}} \quad and \quad \underline{\mu}_{\text{Riemann}} \leqslant \underline{\mu}_{\text{Lebesgue}},$$

so that

$$\underline{\mu}_{\text{Riemann}} \leqslant \underline{\mu}_{\text{Lebesgue}} \leqslant \bar{\mu}_{\text{Lebesgue}} \leqslant \bar{\mu}_{\text{Riemann}}.$$

This inequality implies the following:

THEOREM. *Each Riemann-measurable set is Lebesgue-measurable, and its Riemann and Lebesgue measures are equal.*

Conversely, it is not necessary that a Lebesgue-measurable set is Riemann-measurable, as is shown by the set of the rational numbers between 0 and 1, since its one-dimensional measures are:

$$\underline{\mu}_{\text{Riemann}} = 0, \quad \underline{\mu}_{\text{Lebesgue}} = 0,$$

$$\bar{\mu}_{\text{Riemann}} = 1, \quad \bar{\mu}_{\text{Lebesgue}} = 0.$$

As to the proof of the last statement, let $r_1, r_2, \ldots$ be an enumeration of the set of all the rational numbers concerned (see Theorem 2.5) and cover r_ν by any open interval of length $\epsilon/2^\nu$ where ϵ denotes any positive number. Then

$$\bar{\mu}_{\text{Lebesgue}} \leqslant \epsilon \sum_{\nu=1}^{\infty} 2^{-\nu} = \epsilon;$$

hence $\bar{\mu}_{\text{Lebesgue}} = 0.$

§ 8. The Lebesgue integral

8.1. DEFINITIONS. Let L be a Lebesgue subset of R^n of finite measure, and

$$L = L_1 + L_2 + \ldots + L_k$$

where $L_1, L_2, \ldots, L_k$ are any Lebesgue subsets of L such that the intersections of any two of them are empty. Further, let $f(x)$ be a scalar function of x defined and bounded in L, its lower bound in L_κ be denoted by m_κ and its upper bound in L_κ by M_κ. Then the expressions

$$\sum_{\kappa=1}^{k} m_\kappa \cdot \mu L_\kappa \quad \text{and} \quad \sum_{\kappa=1}^{k} M_\kappa \cdot \mu L_\kappa$$

are called the lower and the upper *Darboux sums* of the function $f(x)$ with respect to the division of the set L into the sets $L_1, \ldots, L_k$.

The upper bound of all the lower Darboux sums obtained by any division of L into a finite number of subsets is called the *lower integral* of $f(x)$ over L and denoted by $(L)\underline{\int} f(x)\,\mathrm{d}x$; correspondingly, the lower bound of all the upper Darboux sums is called the *upper integral* of $f(x)$ and denoted by $(L)\overline{\int} f(x)\,\mathrm{d}x$. Evidently, $\underline{\int} f(x)\,\mathrm{d}x \leqslant \overline{\int} f(x)\,\mathrm{d}x$.

If the lower and the upper integral over the set L are equal, the function $f(x)$ is said to be integrable over L, and the common value of both integrals is called the *(Lebesgue) integral* of the function $f(x)$ over the set L. It is denoted by $\displaystyle\int_L f(x)\,\mathrm{d}x$.

A scalar function $f(x)$ defined in a subset S of R^n is said to be *Lebesgue-measurable* in S if, for any value of C, the set of all points x of S for which $f(x) \leqslant C$ is Lebesgue-measurable. If all these sets are even Borel sets, then the function $f(x)$ is called

Borel-measurable. For example, continuous functions are Borel-measurable by Theorems 5.3 and 7.8.

8.2. For Riemann-measurable sets, *Riemann integrals* can be defined in an analogous fashion by replacing the divisions of L into Lebesgue sets by divisions into Riemann-measurable sets. Since, by § 7.6, every Riemann-measurable set is Lebesgue-measurable, the aggregate of all Riemann divisions is a sub-aggregate of all Lebesgue divisions. Hence

$$\left.\begin{array}{l} \bar{\int}\text{Riemann} \geqslant \bar{\int}\text{Lebesgue,} \\ \underline{\int}\text{Riemann} \leqslant \underline{\int}\text{Lebesgue.} \end{array}\right\}$$

In a way similar to § 7.6, these inequalities imply the following:

THEOREM. *If a function is Riemann-integrable over any Riemann set, it is also Lebesgue-integrable over this set, and both integrals are equal.*

8.3. THEOREMS. If L is a Lebesgue set of finite measure and the functions $f(x)$ and $g(x)$ are Lebesgue-integrable over L, then also their sum $f(x)+g(x)$ is integrable over L, and

$$\int_L \{f(x)+g(x)\}\,\mathrm{d}x = \int_L f(x)\,\mathrm{d}x + \int_L g(x)\,\mathrm{d}x.$$

If both the Lebesgue sets L_1 and L_2 of finite measures have no common points, and if the function $f(x)$ is integrable over L_1 and L_2, it is integrable over L_1+L_2, too, and

$$\int_{L_1+L_2} f(x)\,\mathrm{d}x = \int_{L_1} f(x)\,\mathrm{d}x + \int_{L_2} f(x)\,\mathrm{d}x.$$

If the function $f(x)$ is integrable over the Lebesgue set L of finite measure, then the function $c.f(x)$ where c denotes any constant is integrable over L, too, and

$$\int_L c.f(x)\,\mathrm{d}x = c.\int_L f(x)\,\mathrm{d}x.$$

Further, if $m \leqslant f(x) \leqslant M$ for $x \in L,$

then $m.\mu L \leqslant \displaystyle\int_L f(x)\,\mathrm{d}x \leqslant M\mu L.$

In particular, the integral over a set of measure 0 always vanishes. The proofs follow immediately from Definitions 8.1.

8.4. THEOREM. *If the (bounded) function $f(x)$ is Lebesgue-measurable in the Lebesgue set L of finite measure, then both $f(x)$ and $|f(x)|$ are Lebesgue-integrable over each Lebesgue subset L' of L, and*

$$\left| \int_{L'} f(x)\,\mathrm{d}x \right| \leqslant \int_{L'} |f(x)|\,\mathrm{d}x.$$

Conversely, if the bounded function $f(x)$ is integrable over the Lebesgue set L of finite measure, $f(x)$ is Lebesgue-measurable in L.

Proof. Cover the set of all values of $f(x)$ by a sequence of half-open intervals of length ϵ. To each interval, there corresponds a Lebesgue subset of L such that the values which $f(x)$ takes in this set belong to the interval. The difference of the corresponding Darboux sums is $\leqslant \epsilon \cdot \mu L$; hence it can be made arbitrarily small. The integral

$$\int_{L'} f(x)\,\mathrm{d}x$$

therefore exists. The rest of the proof is similar.

8.5. APPROXIMATION THEOREM. *If the bounded function $f(x)$ is integrable over the Lebesgue set L of finite measure, it can be uniformly approximated in L by integrable piecewise constant functions (i.e. by integrable functions which take only a finite number of values).*

The proof is similar to that of Theorem 8.4.

8.6. THEOREM. *The sum and the product of a finite or enumerable number of Lebesgue- (or Borel-) measurable functions which are all defined in the same subset L of R^n are Lebesgue- (or Borel-) measurable.*

Proof for the sum of two Lebesgue-measurable functions $f(x)$ and $g(x)$. Define the sets U_c and V_c by

$$f(x) \leqslant c \text{ if (and only if) } x \in U_c, \\ g(x) \leqslant c \text{ if (and only if) } x \in V_c, \Big\}$$

where c is any number, and define the sets W_γ and W by

$$\left.\begin{aligned}
W_\gamma &= \sum_{\alpha+\beta \leqslant \gamma} U_\alpha V_\beta, \\
W &= \prod_{\gamma > c} W_\gamma,
\end{aligned}\right\}$$

where α, β, γ denote any rational numbers which satisfy the conditions that $\gamma > c$ and $\alpha+\beta \leqslant \gamma$. The meaning of the right-hand sides of the definitions of W_γ and W is as follows. The set of the numbers γ is enumerable (cf. Theorem 2.5). Let $\gamma_1, \gamma_2, \ldots$ be any of its enumerations. Then the symbol $\prod\limits_{\gamma > c} W_\gamma$ means the intersection $W_{\gamma_1} W_{\gamma_2} \ldots$. The meaning of the symbol $\sum\limits_{\alpha+\beta \leqslant \gamma} U_\alpha V_\beta$ is explained in a similar manner.

Now, if $f(x)+g(x) \leqslant c$, then $x \in W$. For, $x \in W_\gamma$, for any admitted value of γ. Conversely, if x is any fixed element of W, then $f(x)+g(x) \leqslant c$. For

$$x \in \sum_{\alpha+\beta \leqslant \gamma_i} U_\alpha V_\beta, \quad i = 1, 2, \ldots.$$

Hence, for each value of i there are two rational α_i, β_i such that

$$x \in U_{\alpha_i} V_{\beta_i}$$

and $\alpha_i + \beta_i \leqslant \gamma_i$. Therefore,

$$\left.\begin{aligned}
f(x) &\leqslant \alpha_i, \\
g(x) &\leqslant \beta_i,
\end{aligned}\right\}$$

from which it follows that

$$f(x)+g(x) \leqslant \alpha_i + \beta_i \leqslant \gamma_i, \quad i = 1, 2, \ldots$$

and, finally, $$f(x)+g(x) \leqslant \liminf_{\gamma > c} \gamma = c.$$

Thus $$f(x)+g(x) \leqslant c$$
if and only if $x \in W$.

Now, the set W is composed of Lebesgue sets U_α and V_β by means of an enumerable number of intersections and additions. Hence it is a Lebesgue set itself (cf. Theorem 7.3).

Q.E.D.

COROLLARY. The limit of a convergent sequence of continuous functions is Borel-measurable.

8.7. DEFINITIONS. If a statement is true for all points x of a set S except those of a subset of S of measure 0, the statement is said to be true for "*almost all*" points x of S. If a function $f(x)$ is integrable over a Lebesgue set L' which is a subset of the Lebesgue set L, and if $\mu(L-L') = 0$, the integral $\int_L f(x)\, \mathrm{d}x$ is in any case to be understood as the integral $\int_{L'} f(x)\, \mathrm{d}x$ (whether or not $f(x)$ may be defined in $L-L'$).

8.8. THEOREM. *Let the (bounded) functions* $f_1(x), f_2(x), \ldots$ *be integrable over the Lebesgue set* L *of finite measure. Further, assume that the series* $\sum\limits_{\nu=1}^{\infty} f_\nu(x)$ *converges in almost all points* x *of* L *and that its partial sums are uniformly bounded in* L *by a positive constant* K. *Then the function* $f(x) = \sum\limits_{\nu=1}^{\infty} f_\nu(x)$ *is integrable over* L, *and*

$$\int_L f(x)\, \mathrm{d}x = \sum_{\nu=1}^{\infty} \int_L f_\nu(x)\, \mathrm{d}x.$$

Note. There is a corresponding proposition about sequences of functions $g_1(x), g_2(x), \ldots$ which is equivalent to the theorem. In order to see this, put

$$
\begin{aligned}
f_1 &= g_1, \\
f_2 &= g_2 - g_1, \\
f_3 &= g_3 - g_2, \\
&\ldots\ldots\ldots\ldots
\end{aligned}
\qquad \text{or} \qquad
\begin{aligned}
g_1 &= f_1, \\
g_2 &= f_1 + f_2, \\
g_3 &= f_1 + f_2 + f_3, \\
&\ldots\ldots\ldots\ldots\ldots
\end{aligned}
$$

Proof. By Theorems 8.4 and 8.6, $f_1(x), f_2(x), \ldots$ and $f(x)$ are Lebesgue-measurable, hence $f(x)$ is integrable, again by Theorem 8.4. Now

$$\left| \int_L g_\lambda(x)\, \mathrm{d}x - \int_L f(x)\, \mathrm{d}x \right| \leqslant \int_L |g_\lambda(x) - f(x)|\, \mathrm{d}x,$$

where $g_1(x), g_2(x), \ldots$ are the partial sums of the series $\sum\limits_{\nu=1}^{\infty} f_\nu(x)$. Let ϵ be any positive constant, and L_λ the set of all the points x of L for which

$$|g_\lambda(x) - f(x)| < \epsilon.$$

Put
$$M_l = \sum_{\lambda=1}^{l} L_\lambda.$$

Evidently,
$$\lim_{l \to \infty} \mu(L - M_l) = 0.$$

Now

$$\left| \int_L g_l(x)\,\mathrm{d}x - \int_L f(x)\,\mathrm{d}x \right| \leqslant \int_{M_l} |g_l - f|\,\mathrm{d}x + \int_{L - M_l} |g_l - f|\,\mathrm{d}x$$

$$\leqslant \epsilon . \mu L + 2K\mu(L - M_l),$$

since K is an upper bound of the partial sums. Hence

$$\lim_{l \to \infty} \left| \int_L g_l\,\mathrm{d}x - \int_L f\,\mathrm{d}x \right| = 0.$$

Q.E.D.

8.9. THEOREM. *Let $\{L_1, L_2, ...\}$ be a finite or enumerable aggregate of Lebesgue sets no two of which have common points, and assume that their sum has a finite measure. If then the (bounded) function $f(x)$ is integrable over each of the sets $L_1, L_2, ...$, so it is over the set $L_1 + L_2 + ...$, and*

$$\int_{L_1 + L_2 + ...} f(x)\,\mathrm{d}x = \int_{L_1} f(x)\,\mathrm{d}x + \int_{L_2} f(x)\,\mathrm{d}x + ...$$

Proof. Let $\delta_\lambda(x)$ denote the characteristic function of the set L_λ:

$$\delta_\lambda(x) = \begin{cases} 1 & \text{if} \quad x \in L_\lambda, \\ 0 & \text{if} \quad x \in R^n - L_\lambda. \end{cases}$$

Then
$$f(x) = \sum_\lambda f(x)\,\delta_\lambda(x) \quad \text{if} \quad x \in L_1 + L_2 + ...$$

Now apply Theorem 8.8.

8.10. So far, only bounded functions and sets of finite measures have been admitted. Both these restrictions will now be removed.

DEFINITIONS. Let L be a Lebesgue set of finite measure and $f(x)$ a function which is Lebesgue-measurable in L, but not necessarily bounded. Define an auxiliary function $f_{\alpha\beta}(x)$ which is measurable and bounded in L by

$$f_{\alpha\beta}(x) = \begin{cases} \alpha & \text{if } f(x) < \alpha, \\ f(x) & \text{if } \alpha \leqslant f(x) \leqslant \beta, \\ \beta & \text{if } f(x) > \beta, \end{cases}$$

where α, β denote any two constants such that $\alpha < \beta$. The function $f(x)$ is said to be integrable over L if there is a (finite) limit

$$\lim_{\substack{\alpha \to -\infty \\ \beta \to +\infty}} \int_L f_{\alpha\beta}(x)\,dx,$$

and the integral $\int_L f(x)\,dx$ is defined by this limit.

Now let J be the interval

$$a_\nu \leqslant x_\nu \leqslant b_\nu, \quad \nu = 1, 2, \ldots, n,$$

L a Lebesgue subset of R^n not necessarily of finite measure, and $f(x)$ a function which is Lebesgue-measurable in L. Then the function $f(x)$ is said to be integrable over L if there is a (finite) limit $\lim \int_{L.J.} f(x)\,dx$ for

$$\left. \begin{array}{l} a_\nu \to -\infty, \\ b_\nu \to +\infty, \end{array} \right\} \nu = 1, 2, \ldots, n.$$

The integral $\int_L f(x)\,dx$ is defined by this limit.

8.11. Nearly all the previous propositions of this section are true for unbounded functions and sets of infinite measures, too. The only important exceptions occur in Theorems 8.4 and 8.5; a Lebesgue-measurable function need no longer be integrable. For example, the function x is not integrable over the positive x-axis though it is Lebesgue-measurable in it. The approximation theorem 8.5 can be generalized in two ways: either an integrable function $f(x)$ can be uniformly approximated by a function which takes only a finite or enumerable number of values, or $f(x)$ can be approximated by an integrable piecewise constant function $c(x)$ such that $\int_{R^n} |c(x) - f(x)|\,dx$ is arbitrarily small. Theorem 8.8 still holds when the partial sums of $\sum\limits_{1}^{\infty} f_\nu(x)$ are bounded by any function integrable over L.

8.12. In the following the indefinite Lebesgue integral is to be considered.

DEFINITIONS. Let A be an additive class of subsets of R^n. Then a correspondence of real numbers $F(S)$ to the sets S of A is called a *set function* defined in A. It is said to be *additive* if, for a finite number of sets $S_1, S_2, ..., S_k$ of A, no two of which have common points,

$$F(S_1 + S_2 + ... + S_k) = F(S_1) + ... + F(S_k).$$

If A is the set of all Lebesgue sets L and the corresponding equation is true for every enumerable aggregate $\{L_1, L_2, ...\}$ such that $\mu(L_1 + L_2 ...)$ is finite, then the function $F(L)$ is called *absolutely additive*. A set function $F(L)$ defined for all Lebesgue sets L is said to be *absolutely continuous* if, for every positive constant ϵ, there is a positive constant $\delta(\epsilon)$ such that

$$|F(L)| < \epsilon$$

for each Lebesgue set L whose measure $\mu L < \delta(\epsilon)$.

Examples. μL and $\int_L f(x)\,\mathrm{d}x$ are absolutely continuous and absolutely additive set functions if the point function $f(x)$ is integrable over each Lebesgue subset of R^n of finite measure.

8.13. THEOREM. *Let $F(L)$ be an absolutely continuous additive set function which is defined for all Lebesgue subsets of R^n and finite for all sets of finite measure. Then $F(L)$ is absolutely additive.*

Proof. Let $L_1, L_2, ...$ be sets without mutual intersections such that μL is finite where $L = L_1 + L_2 + ...$. Then

$$\left| F(L) - \sum_{\kappa=1}^{k} F(L_\kappa) \right| = |F(L_{k+1} + L_{k+2} + ...)|$$

and
$$\mu(L_{k+1} + L_{k+2} + ...) = \mu L - \sum_{\kappa=1}^{k} \mu L_\kappa.$$

Hence, for sufficiently large values of k, the value of

$$\mu(L_{k+1} + L_{k+2} + ...)$$

becomes arbitrarily small, and so does the value of

$$F(L_{k+1} + L_{k+2} + \dots),$$

on account of the absolute continuity of $F(L)$.

Therefore, $F(L) - \sum_{k=1}^{\infty} F(L_k) = 0.$

Q.E.D.

8.14. THEOREM. *Let $F(L)$ be an absolutely continuous additive set function defined for all Lebesgue subsets of L of R^n. Then there is a point function $f(x)$ defined at almost all points x of R^n such that, for each set L of finite measure, the integral $\int_L f(x)\,dx$ exists and*

$$F(L) = \int_L f(x)\,dx.$$

The function $f(x)$ is uniquely determined almost everywhere in R^n.
The proof of the uniqueness is indirect. If there were two different functions $f_1(x)$ and $f_2(x)$, the integral of their difference over any Lebesgue subset of R^n would vanish. This is possible only if they coincide almost everywhere.

A function $f(x)$ can be constructed in the following fashion. Let $C_a(x)$ be the cube of edge length a and centre x. Then

$$\liminf_{a \to 0} \frac{F\{C_a(x)\}}{\mu C_a(x)} \quad \text{and} \quad \limsup_{a \to 0} \frac{F\{C_a(x)\}}{\mu C_a(x)}$$

are integrable over any Lebesgue set L of finite measure, and their integrals are equal to $F(L)$. (For the details, see the literature, e.g. Carathéodory's book.)

8.15. FUBINI'S THEOREM. *Let the function $f(x^1, x^2)$, where $x^1 \in R^{n_1}$, $x^2 \in R^{n_2}$, be integrable over $R^{n_1} \times R^{n_2}$. Then the integrals*

$$\int_{R^{n_1}} f(x^1, x^2)\,dx^1 \quad \text{and} \quad \int_{R^{n_2}} f(x^1, x^2)\,dx^2$$

exist for almost all points x^2 of R^{n_2} and x^1 of R^{n_1}, respectively, and so do the integrals

$$\int_{R^{n_2}} \left[\int_{R^{n_1}} f(x^1, x^2)\,dx^1 \right] dx^2 \quad \text{and} \quad \int_{R^{n_1}} \left[\int_{R^{n_2}} f(x^1, x^2)\,dx^2 \right] dx^1.$$

Further,

$$\int_{R^{n_2}} \left[\int_{R^{n_1}} f(x^1, x^2) \, dx^1 \right] dx^2 = \int_{R^{n_1+n_2}} f(x^1, x^2) \, d(x^1, x^2)$$

$$= \int_{R^{n_1}} \left[\int_{R^{n_2}} f(x^1, x^2) \, dx^2 \right] dx^1.$$

Outline of the proof. Approximate, according to § 8.5 or § 8.11, the function $f(x^1, x^2)$ by a piecewise constant function

$$\sum_{\rho=1}^{r} c_\rho \, \delta_{L_\rho} (x^1, x^2),$$

where the L_ρ's are Lebesgue subsets of $R^{n_1+n_2}$, the symbol δ denotes characteristic functions, and the c_ρ's are constants. Thus it is sufficient to consider characteristic functions $\delta_L(x^1, x^2)$. If L is an interval or the sum of intervals, the statement is evident. By limiting processes, it is extended to Borel sets. A general Lebesgue set is approximated by two Borel sets, A and B, according to Theorem 7.5, and an application of Theorem 8.13 now yields the theorem.

8.16. THEOREM. *If for a function* $f(x^1, x^2)$ *the integrals*

$$\int_{R^{n_1}} f(x^1, x^2) \, dx^1$$

(*for almost all* x^2 *of* R^{n_2}) *and*

$$\int_{R^{n_2}} \left[\int_{R^{n_1}} f(x^1, x^2) \, dx^1 \right] dx^2$$

exist, so do the integrals

$$\int_{R^{n_1+n_2}} f(x^1, x^2) \, d(x^1, x^2) \quad \text{and} \quad \int_{R^{n_2}} f(x^1, x^2) \, dx^2,$$

the latter for almost all x^1 *of* R^{n_1}. (For the proof, see the literature.)

§ 9. Hilbert spaces

Most of the contents of this section will be needed only for the proofs of v. Neumann's theorems 13.3 and 13.4.

9.1. DEFINITIONS. A set R of elements $f, g, h, \ldots$ is called a (real) *linear space* if it satisfies the following conditions:

(i) To each pair of elements f and g of R, there corresponds a unique element h which is called the sum of the elements f and g and denoted by $f+g$, so that

$$h = f+g.$$

The addition of elements of R is assumed to be commutative and associative. This means that

$$f_1+f_2 = f_2+f_1,$$
$$(f_1+f_2)+f_3 = f_1+(f_2+f_3),$$

for any elements f_1,f_2,f_3 of R. (Hence we are entitled to speak simply of the sum of the three elements f_1,f_2,f_3 and to denote it by $f_1+f_2+f_3$ without brackets.)

(ii) To each element f of R and each real number α, there corresponds an element of R which is called the product of α and f and denoted by αf, $\alpha.f$, $f.\alpha$ or $f\alpha$. For this multiplication the following rules are supposed to be valid:

$$1.f = f,$$
$$(\alpha+\beta)f = \alpha f+\beta f,$$
$$\alpha(f+g) = \alpha f+\alpha g,$$
$$\alpha(\beta f) = (\alpha\beta)f,$$

for any elements f,g of R and any real numbers α and β.

Examples. The set of all functions which are defined and bounded in R^n; the set of all continuous functions in R^n; the set of all functions which are Lebesgue-integrable over a given subset of R^n.

A linear space R is called a (real) *Hilbert space* if it satisfies the following conditions:

(i) To each pair of elements f and g of R, there corresponds a real number which is called the product of the elements f and g and denoted by (f,g). The following laws shall hold for it:

$$(f,g) = (g,f),$$
$$(f_1+f_2,g) = (f_1,g)+(f_2,g),$$
$$(f,f)\begin{cases} > 0 & \text{if } f \neq 0, \\ = 0 & \text{if } f = 0, \end{cases}$$
$$(\alpha f,g) = \alpha(f,g),$$

for any elements f, g, f_1, f_2 of R and any real number α.

(ii) If the sequence $f_1, f_2, \ldots$ of elements of R is a "Cauchy sequence", i.e. if

$$(f_{k+p} - f_k, f_{k+p} - f_k) < \epsilon$$

for each $k > k_0(\epsilon)$ and each $p = 1, 2, \ldots$, then the sequence $f_1, f_2, \ldots$ converges towards an element f of R, i.e. there is an element f of R such that

$$(f_l - f, f_l - f) < \epsilon \quad \text{for} \quad l > l_0(\epsilon).$$

Example. The vector space R where the product of two vectors x and y is defined as in § 4.1 by the bilinear expression $\sum_{\nu=1}^{n} x_\nu y_\nu$.

Two elements the product of which vanishes are said to be *orthogonal* (to each other). The expression $|\sqrt{(f,f)}|$ is called the *norm* of f and denoted by $\|f\|$.

9.2. THEOREMS. Let f and g be two elements of a linear space R in which a multiplication of elements is defined according to condition (i) in the definition 9.1 of the Hilbert space. Then

$$|(f,g)| \leqslant \|f\| \cdot \|g\| \quad \text{(Schwarz' inequality)},$$

$$\|f+g\| \leqslant \|f\| + \|g\| \quad \text{(triangular inequality)},$$

$$\|f+g\|^2 + \|f-g\|^2 = 2(\|f\|^2 + \|g\|^2).$$

The *proofs* of both the first relations are similar to those of Theorems 4.2 and 4.3. The third statement can be directly confirmed by the computation of the left-hand side.

9.3. Let $w(x)$ be a non-negative function defined in R^n such that $\int_{R^n} w(x)\,\mathrm{d}x$ exists and is positive. Without any essential loss of generality, it may be assumed that

$$\int_{R^n} w(x)\,\mathrm{d}x = 1.$$

Further, let $f(x)$ and $g(x)$ be any functions which are defined and Lebesgue-measurable in R^n and for which the integrals

$$\int_{R^n} f^2 w\,\mathrm{d}x \quad \text{and} \quad \int_{R^n} g^2 w\,\mathrm{d}x$$

exist. Then also the integrals

$$\int_{R^n} |f(x)g(x)| w(x)\,\mathrm{d}x \quad \text{and} \quad \int_{R^n} f(x)g(x)w(x)\,\mathrm{d}x$$

exist. (This can be shown in a manner similar to that used in the proof of Schwarz' inequality.) Hence the functions $f(x)$ which are Lebesgue-measurable in R^n and for which the integrals $\int_{R^n} f^2 w\,\mathrm{d}x$ exist form a linear space R. Now define a "product" (f,g) for any two elements f,g of R by

$$(f,g) = \int_{R^n} f(x)g(x)w(x)\,\mathrm{d}x.$$

It is a product in the sense of condition (i) in Definition 9.1 of a Hilbert space if the convention is made that two functions $f(x)$ and $f'(x)$ which differ only on a subset N of R^n such that

$$\int_N w(x)\,\mathrm{d}x = 0,$$

are to be considered as not essentially different.

Evidently the relation of "not being essentially different" is a transitive relation: if it holds for both pairs of functions f,f' and f',f'', it also holds for the pair f,f''. So the space R can be divided into classes of "equivalent" functions such that any two functions of a given class are not essentially different.

The set of these classes is a linear space if the addition of classes is defined by the corresponding addition of its members. Similarly, a multiplication of classes can be defined. Moreover, *the set of these classes is a Hilbert space*. With respect to functions, this means:

THEOREM. *The set R of all the functions $f(x)$ which are Lebesgue-measurable in R^n and for which $\int_{R^n} [f(x)]^2 w(x)\,\mathrm{d}x$ exists is a Hilbert space if the product (f,g) of any two of its elements f,g is defined by*

$$(f,g) = \int_{R^n} f(x)g(x)w(x)\,\mathrm{d}x.$$

Any two functions the difference of which differs from zero only in a set N for which

$$\int_N w(x)\,\mathrm{d}x = 0$$

are here to be considered as not essentially different.

Proof. By the Schwarz and Triangular Inequalities (9.2), it is shown that R is a linear space. The essential part of the proof is the demonstration that each Cauchy sequence of elements $f_1, f_2, \ldots$ of R converges towards an element f of R. This element can be constructed in the following manner. Since, by the assumption

$$\|f_{k+p} - f_k\|^2 < \epsilon \quad \text{if} \quad k > k_0(\epsilon), \quad p = 1, 2, 3, \ldots,$$

there is a sub-sequence $f_{k_1}, f_{k_2}, \ldots$ such that

$$\|f_{k_{j+p}} - f_{k_j}\|^2 < \frac{1}{2^{3j}} \quad \text{if} \quad k_j > k_0\left(\frac{1}{2^{3j}}\right), \quad p = 1, 2, 3, \ldots .$$

In particular,

$$\|f_{k_{j+1}} - f_{k_j}\|^2 < \frac{1}{2^{3j}} \quad \text{if} \quad k_j > k_0\left(\frac{1}{2^{3j}}\right).$$

Now denote by E_j the (Lebesgue) set of all the points x of R^n such that

$$|f_{k_{j+1}}(x) - f_{k_j}(x)| > \frac{1}{2^j}.$$

Then

$$P(E_j) \equiv \int_{E_j} w(x)\,\mathrm{d}x \leqslant \frac{1}{2^j},$$

as may be proved indirectly. Hence

$$|f_{k_{j+p}}(x) - f_{k_j}(x)| < \sum_{\lambda=0}^{\infty} \frac{1}{2^{j+\lambda}} = \frac{1}{2^{j-1}}$$

if

$$x \in D_j = R^n - \sum_{\lambda=0}^{\infty} E_{j+\lambda},$$

so that, by Cauchy's convergence criterion, the sequence $f_{k_1}, f_{k_2}, \ldots$ converges uniformly on D_j. Now define $f_j^*(x)$ by

$$f_j^*(x) = \begin{cases} \lim_{p \to \infty} f_{k_{j+p}}(x) & \text{if} \quad x \in D_j, \\ 0 & \text{if} \quad x \in R^n - D_j, \end{cases}$$

and $f(x)$ by

$$f(x) = \lim_{j \to \infty} f_j^*(x) \text{ for all } x \text{ of } R^n.$$

The sets $D_1, D_2, D_3, \ldots$ form a monotonic increasing sequence such that $$D_1 \subseteq D_2 \subseteq D_3 \subseteq \ldots$$

and $$\lim_{j \to \infty} P(R^n - D_j) = 0.$$

From this, the Triangular Inequality (9.2) and Theorem 8.8, it follows that f is an element of R. Further,

$$\|f_l - f\| \leqslant \|f_l - f_{k_{j+p}}\| + \|f_{k_{j+p}} - f_j^*\| + \|f_j^* - f\|$$

(by 9.2). For sufficiently large values of j, p and l, the right-hand side is arbitrarily small.   Q.E.D.

9.4. Definitions. Let a be any element of the Hilbert space R and ϵ any positive constant. Then the set of all elements f of R for which $\|f - a\| < \epsilon$ is called an (ϵ-)*neighbourhood* of a. (Cf. the analogous Definition 4.1.)

An element h of R is said to be a *limiting element* of the subset S of R if in every neighbourhood of h there is at least one element of S which is different from h.

A subset L of R is said to be *linear* if, for any two elements f, g of L and for arbitrary real numbers α, β, the element $\alpha f + \beta g$ always belongs to L.

The sum of a linear subset L and the set of its limiting elements is called a *linear sub-space* of R and denoted by $\bar{L}$. Evidently, $\bar{L}$ is a Hilbert space.

9.5. Theorem. *Let $\bar{L}$ be a linear sub-space of a Hilbert space R and f any element of R. Then f can always be represented in the form*

$$f = g + h$$

where g is a uniquely determined element of $\bar{L}$ and h is orthogonal to each element of $\bar{L}$. (See the figure.)

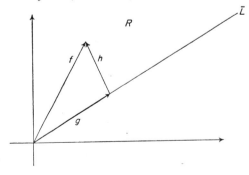

Proof. If there were two such representations $f = g_1 + h_1$ and $f = g_2 + h_2$, then $g_1 - g_2 = h_2 - h_1$ and

$$(g_1 - g_2, h_2 - h_1) = (h_2 - h_1, h_2 - h_1).$$

Since the left-hand side vanishes (on account of the ortho-gonality of its factors), $h_2 = h_1$ and, therefore, $g_2 = g_1$. This proves the uniqueness of the representation. In order to show its existence, let ϕ be an arbitrary element of $\bar{L}$. Then the set of all the non-negative numbers $\| \phi - f \|$ has a lower bound $\delta \geqslant 0$. There is even an element ϕ^* of $\bar{L}$ such that $\| \phi^* - f \| = \delta$. For let $\epsilon_1, \epsilon_2, \ldots$ be a sequence of positive numbers tending towards zero, then, for each positive integer $k = 1, 2, \ldots$, there is an element ϕ_k of $\bar{L}$ such that

$$\| \phi_k - f \| < \delta + \epsilon_k.$$

Now, by the third statement of Theorem 9.2,

$$\| \phi_{k+p} - \phi_k \|^2 = \| (\phi_{k+p} - f) - (\phi_k - f) \|^2$$
$$\leqslant 2 \| \phi_{k+p} - f \|^2 + 2 \| \phi_k - f \|^2 - \| (\phi_{k+p} - f) + (\phi_k - f) \|^2.$$

The last term equals

$$4 \| \tfrac{1}{2}(\phi_{k+p} - \phi_k) - f \|^2;$$

this is $\geqslant 4\delta^2$ since $\tfrac{1}{2}(\phi_{k+p} - \phi_k)$ is an element of $\bar{L}$. Hence

$$\| \phi_{k+p} - \phi_k \|^2 \leqslant 2(\delta + \epsilon_{k+p})^2 + 2(\delta + \epsilon_k)^2 - 4\delta^2,$$

and from this it follows by Cauchy's criterion that the sequence $\phi_1, \phi_2, \ldots$ converges towards a uniquely determined element ϕ^* of $\bar{L}$. Now, by the triangular inequality (9.2),

$$\| \phi^* - f \| \leqslant \| \phi^* - \phi_k \| + \| \phi_k - f \|,$$

and, therefore, for $k \to \infty$,

$$\| \phi^* - f \| = \delta.$$

Now it will be shown that $f - \phi^*$ is orthogonal to each element ϕ of $\bar{L}$. With ϕ, $\phi^* + \alpha\phi$ also belongs to $\bar{L}$ for each value of α. Therefore,

$$\| (\phi^* - f) + \alpha\phi \|^2 = \| (\phi^* + \alpha\phi) - f \|^2 \geqslant \| \phi^* - f \|^2.$$

Since the left-hand side equals

$$\| \phi^* - f \|^2 + 2\alpha(\phi^* - f, \phi) + \alpha^2 \| \phi \|^2,$$

this inequality reduces to

$$2\alpha(\phi^* - f, \phi) + \alpha^2 \| \phi \|^2 \geqslant 0$$

for every value of α and, in particular, for

$$\alpha = -\frac{(\phi^* - f, \phi)}{\| \phi \|^2}.$$

(The case $\| \phi \| = 0$ can be excluded as trivial.) Therefore,

$$-(\phi^* - f, \phi)^2 \geqslant 0$$

and, finally, $\quad\quad\quad\quad (\phi^* - f, \phi) = 0,$

as has been stated. Now put

$$\left. \begin{aligned} g &= \phi^*, \\ h &= f - \phi^*, \end{aligned} \right\}$$

and the proof of the theorem is complete.

References

A concise presentation of the "naïve" theory of sets (as applied in this book) is given by

[1] KAMKE, E., *Mengenlehre*, Berlin, 1947. There is an English translation, published in 1950 in New York.

The foundations and the axiomatics of the set theory are dealt with in all details by

[2] FRÄNKEL, A., *Einleitung in die Mengenlehre* (Springer). Several editions, e.g., 1928 and later.

There is a more recent presentation of this subject by the same author:

[3] FRÄNKEL, A., *Abstract Set Theory*, Amsterdam, 1953.

This book, however, is not known to me through my own study. The following book deeply influenced the development of the theory of point sets:

[4] HAUSDORFF, F., *Grundzüge der Mengenlehre*, Berlin, 1914.

There have been several subsequent editions, including some quite recent ones. Some of the different editions differ considerably as Hausdorff used different systems of axioms.
Another, very readable, presentation of the subject is the book

[5] SIERPINSKI, W., *General Topology*, Toronto, 1952.

As to differential equations, see

[6] KAMKE, E., *Differentialgleichungen reeller Funktionen*, Leipzig, 1930.

More general assumptions about the right-hand sides of the equations are made in the relevant chapters of the following books:

[7] CARATHÉODORY, C., *Vorlesungen über reelle Funktionen*, Leipzig, 1929.

[8] MCSHANE, E. J., *Integration* (Princeton University Press), 1944.

Their principal subject, however, is the theory of the Lebesgue measure and integral. A commendable older presentation of this theory is that by

[9] SCHLESINGER, L., and PLESSNER, A., *Lebesguesche Integrale und Fonriersche Reihen*, Berlin and Leipzig, 1926.

Even more readable (though less exhaustive) may be the introduction to the Lebesgue Theory offered by

[10] CRAMÈR, H., *Mathematical Methods of Statistics* (Princeton University Press). Several editions since 1946.

On the Hilbert space, see, for example,

[11] BÉLA V. SZ. NAGY, *Spektraldarstellung linearer Transformatione des Hilbertschen Raumes*, Berlin, 1942.

The following little book provides considerably easier reading:

[12] SCHMEIDLER, W., *Lineare Operatoren im Hilbertschen Raum*, Stuttgart, 1954.

Details of the proof of Theorem 9.3 may be found in the following books:

[14] V. NEUMANN, J., *Mathematische Grundlagen der Quantenmechanik*, Leipzig, 1932.

[15] ACHIESER, N. J., *Theory of Approximation*, New York, 1956.

CHAPTER III

THE PHASE FLOWS OF
MECHANICAL SYSTEMS

§ 10. Mechanical systems

The concept of a mechanical system will not be defined, but will be supposed known as an elementary idea. Those of its characteristics which will be used in the following will be formally described by postulates, and no assumptions about mechanical systems shall be admitted other than those explicitly formulated. This is not to say that the postulates "define" the concept; on the contrary: the concept is already given to us (though more or less vaguely), and then the postulates are used to stipulate clearly and to catalogue which of its parts are to be used in the deductive theory.

This view of the nature of an axiom resembles Euclid's "classical" concept more than the modern idea coined by Hilbert. The difference, however, is significant only from the point of view of understanding the logical character of the theory and, in particular, its foundations. There is no difference in their logical structure. In both cases the same rules of deductive reasoning have to be applied, starting from the same foundations (i.e. axioms or postulates).

10.1. Postulates. For each *mechanical system* there is a system of ordinary differential equations of the first order,

$$\dot{x}_\nu = X_\nu(x, t), \quad \nu = 1, 2, \ldots, n,$$

which are called the *equations of motion* of the system. Here the symbol t denotes the time variable and a dot denotes differentiation with respect to t. The n-dimensional vector x characterizes the ("microscopic") *state* of the system uniquely. The functions $X_\nu(x, t)$ are supposed to be defined for all values of (x, t) and to possess derivatives with respect to $x_1, \ldots, x_n$ which are continuous functions of (x, t) everywhere in R^{n+1}.

47

The equations of motion are to have a unique solution

$$x = \chi(\overset{o}{x}, \overset{o}{t}, t)$$

which satisfies the arbitrary initial condition

$$\overset{o}{x} = \chi(\overset{o}{x}, \overset{o}{t}, \overset{o}{t})$$

and is defined for all values of $\overset{o}{x}$, $\overset{o}{t}$ and t. (Cf. Theorem 6.3.) *Systems of mass-points* are mechanical systems of a particular kind. For a system of n mass-points there is a system of equations of motion of the special form

$$\left.\begin{aligned}
\dot{x}_\nu &= u_\nu, \\
\dot{y}_\nu &= v_\nu, \\
\dot{z}_\nu &= w_\nu, \\
m_\nu \dot{u}_\nu &= X_\nu(u_1, \ldots, z_n, t), \\
m_\nu \dot{v}_\nu &= Y_\nu(u_1, \ldots, z_n, t), \\
m_\nu \dot{w}_\nu &= Z_\nu(u_1, \ldots, z_n, t),
\end{aligned}\right\} \quad \nu = 1, 2, \ldots, n.$$

Here, $m_1, m_2, \ldots, m_n$ are positive constants and are said to be the *masses* of the mass-points. x, y, z are Cartesian coordinates of the *real space*, which is an R^3, and u, v, w (the corresponding linear velocity components) are Cartesian coordinates of another R^3, which is called *velocity space*. There is a one-to-one correspondence between the vectors $(u_1, \ldots, z_n)$ and the states of the system. (For other coordinates, this need not be true; the states then correspond uniquely to the vectors, but not necessarily vice versa. See, for instance, polar coordinates.) The vector (X_ν, Y_ν, Z_ν) is said to be the *force* acting in the νth mass-point (or "particle").

10.2. DEFINITIONS. Let $\dot{x} = X(x, t)$ be the equations of motion of a mechanical system. Then the set of all the vectors x is called its *phase space* Γ, the set of all moments t is called the *time axis* T, the mapping

$$x = \chi(\overset{o}{x}, \overset{o}{t}, t), \quad \overset{o}{t} = \text{const.}, \ t = \text{const.},$$

of the phase space Γ into itself is named a *phase mapping*, the set of all the phase mappings with $-\infty < t < +\infty$ is said to be the *phase flow* χ of the mechanical system, and the set of all the "*phase-points*" $x = \chi(\overset{o}{x}, \overset{o}{t}, t)$ for fixed values of $\overset{o}{x}$ and $\overset{o}{t}$ and

$-\infty < t < +\infty$, is called a *(phase) trajectory* through the initial phase-point $\overset{\circ}{x}$. If the vector X is independent of the time variable t, the phase flow is said to be *stationary*.

A function $\psi(x,t)$ defined in $\Gamma \times T$ is called a *(First) Integral* of the equations of motion or an *invariant function* with respect to the phase flow χ if the function $\psi\{\chi(\overset{\circ}{x},\overset{\circ}{t},t),t\}$ (formally depending on the time variable t) is actually independent of t, i.e. if
$$\psi\{\chi(\overset{\circ}{x},\overset{\circ}{t},t)\} = \psi(\overset{\circ}{x},\overset{\circ}{t})$$
for all $(\overset{\circ}{x},\overset{\circ}{t})$.

10.3. THEOREMS. From
$$x = \chi(\overset{\circ}{x},\overset{\circ}{t},t),$$
it follows that
$$\overset{\circ}{x} = \chi(x,t,\overset{\circ}{t}).$$

Hence *the functions* $\chi_\nu(x,t,\overset{\circ}{t})$ *are invariant with respect to the phase flow* χ. For a stationary phase flow, x is a function of $\overset{\circ}{x}$ and $t-\overset{\circ}{t}$ only. In this case, we simply write
$$x = \chi(\overset{\circ}{x},t-\overset{\circ}{t}).$$
Then
$$\chi\{\chi(\overset{\circ}{x},t_1),t_2\} = \chi(\overset{\circ}{x},t_1+t_2).$$

(The statements are immediate consequences of the Definitions 10.2.)

10.4. DEFINITIONS. Assume that the equations of motion of a given mechanical system can be written in the form
$$\left. \begin{array}{l} \dot{p}_\nu = -H_{q_\nu}(p,q,t), \\ \dot{q}_\nu = +H_{p_\nu}(p,q,t), \end{array} \right\} \quad \nu = 1,2,\ldots,n,$$
where $H_{q_\nu}(p,q,t)$ and $H_{p_\nu}(p,q,t)$ denote the derivatives of a function $H(p,q,t)$ of the variables $p \equiv (p_1,p_2,\ldots,p_n)$, $q \equiv (q_1,q_2,\ldots,q_n)$ and t with respect to q_ν and p_ν. The phase vector $\mathbf{x}$ of the system is $2n$-dimensional and is denoted by (p,q), the p_ν's and q_ν's being its components. Then the mechanical system is called a *Hamiltonian* system, and the same adjective is applied also to its equations of motion and to the function $H(p,q,t)$. By the Postulates 10.1, Hamiltonian functions are always supposed to possess continuous second-order derivatives with respect to the q_ν's and p_ν's.

Equations of motion of a system of n mass-points which have the form

$$\left.\begin{array}{l} \dot{p}_\nu = -V_\nu(q, t), \\ m_\nu \dot{q}_\nu = p_\nu, \end{array}\right\} \quad \nu = 1, \ldots, 3n,$$

where $V_\nu(q, t) \equiv \dfrac{\partial}{\partial q_\nu} V(q, t)$ and $V(q, t) \equiv V(q_1, \ldots, q_n, t)$

are called *Newtonian*. The function $V(q, t)$ (defined for all values of q, t) is named the *potential* or the potential function of the system, and the vectors (p_1, p_2, p_3), (p_4, p_5, p_1), etc. are called the *momenta* of the single particles. (Note that here, at variance with § 10.1, the coordinates of the first particle are denoted by q_1, q_2, q_3, instead of by x_1, y_1, z_1, etc. Further, $m_1 = m_2 = m_3$ and is the mass of the first particle, etc.)

Note. The above definition of Newtonian equations of motion is more restricted than is usual. In general, the equations of motion of § 10.1 for systems of mass-points are called Newton's equations. Here, the additional assumption has been made that there exists a potential function. Systems having no potential play only a minor role in statistical mechanics.

10.5. THEOREMS. *Newtonian equations of motion are Hamiltonian equations, their Hamiltonian function being*

$$\frac{1}{2} \sum_{\nu=1}^{3n} \frac{p_\nu^2}{m_\nu} + V(q, t).$$

If the potential V does not depend on the time variable t, the Hamiltonian function is a First Integral of the equations of motion (called the energy integral).

The first theorem is evident. As for the proof of the second one, insert the general solution of the equations of motion

$$\left.\begin{array}{l} p = \phi(\overset{\circ}{p}, \overset{\circ}{q}, t - \overset{\circ}{t}), \\ q = \psi(\overset{\circ}{p}, \overset{\circ}{q}, t - \overset{\circ}{t}) \end{array}\right\}$$

(cf. § 10.3) into the time-independent Hamiltonian function $H(p, q)$, differentiate with respect to t and express the derivatives $\dot{\phi}, \dot{\psi}$ by the right-hand sides of the equations of motion. The result is that $dH/dt \equiv 0$, which proves the statement.

10.6. DEFINITIONS. Let a mechanical system possess a time-independent Hamiltonian function $H(p,q)$. Then the value of $H(p,q)$ for given p,q is called the *energy* of the system in the state (p,q). For a Newtonian system, the value of the function

$$\frac{1}{2}\sum_{\nu=1}^{3n}\frac{p_\nu^2}{m_\nu}$$

is called the *kinetic energy* of the system in the state (p,q). The kinetic energies of the single particles are defined in a similar manner. The value of the potential is called the *potential energy*. These terms are sometimes also applied to the corresponding functions.

10.7. THEOREMS. Let p^ν and q^ν denote the vectors of momentum and position of the νth particle of a system of mass-points, F^ν be the force acting on it, m^ν its mass. Suppose that F^ν can be represented by the following expression,

$$F^\nu \equiv \sum_{\lambda=1}^{n} f^{\lambda\nu}(|q^\lambda - q^\nu|, t)\frac{q^\lambda - q^\nu}{|q^\lambda - q^\nu|}, \quad \nu = 1, 2, \ldots, n,$$

where the functions $f^{\lambda\nu}(r,t)$ are continuous for $r > 0$, $f^{\lambda\nu} \equiv f^{\nu\lambda}$, $f^{\nu\nu} \equiv 0$ and $f^{\lambda\nu}(0,t) \equiv 0$. Then *the components of the 3-dimensional vectors* $\sum_{\nu=1}^{n} p^\nu$ (the "total momentum" of the system),

$\sum_{\nu=1}^{n}(m^\nu q^\nu - p^\nu t)$ *and* $\sum_{\nu=1}^{n} q^\nu \times p^\nu$ (the "total moment of momentum" of the system) *are First Integrals of the equations of motion.* (Here the symbol $\times$ denotes vector multiplication defined, for instance, by

$$q^1 \times p^1 = \begin{pmatrix} q_1 \\ q_2 \\ q_3 \end{pmatrix} \times \begin{pmatrix} p_1 \\ p_2 \\ p_3 \end{pmatrix} \equiv \begin{pmatrix} q_2 p_3 - q_3 p_2 \\ q_3 p_1 - q_1 p_3 \\ q_1 p_2 - q_2 p_1 \end{pmatrix},$$

etc.) *There is a potential* $V(q,t)$ *for the system, namely,*

$$V(q,t) \equiv \frac{1}{2}\sum_{\lambda=1}^{n}\sum_{\nu=1}^{n} V^{\lambda\nu}(|q^\lambda - q^\nu|, t)$$

where $\qquad\qquad V^{\lambda\nu}(r,t) \equiv -\int f^{\lambda\nu}(r,t)\,dr.$

It contains an arbitrary additive constant. *If all the functions $f^{\lambda \nu}$ are independent of the time variable t, the system has the energy integral*

$$\frac{1}{2} \sum_{\nu=1}^{n} \frac{p^{\nu} p^{\nu}}{m^{\nu}} + \frac{1}{2} \sum_{\lambda=1}^{n} \sum_{\nu=1}^{n} V^{\lambda \nu}(|\, q^{\lambda} - q^{\nu}\,|).$$

Note. The assumption about the particular form of the forces means that, for instance, the force F^1, exerted on the first particle, is the vector sum of all the forces that the mass-points $2, 3, \ldots, n$ exert on mass-point 1; each single force always has one of the two directions of the straight line passing through both the mass-points concerned, and its magnitude depends only on the mutual distance of the particles (and, eventually, on the time variable). Mathematically, these assumptions may appear rather special; but they are simple and seem so plausible that frequently they have been made in attempts to explain complex physical phenomena by simple mechanical models. Cf., for example, the statistical interpretation of the fundamental equations of hydromechanics in § 17.

Outline of the proofs. The existence of the 3×3 First Integrals stated in the theorem is proved in the same manner as the existence of the energy integral in § 10.5. The statement concerning the potential $V(q, t)$ is proved by differentiating $V(q, t)$ with respect to any coordinate q_κ: the result is the negative of the corresponding component of the force. From this and § 10.5 the last statement follows.

§ 11. Phase flow; Liouville's Theorem

According to § 1, the first major difficulty presented by mechanical systems which have a large number of equations of motion is that, in general, the position of its initial point $\overset{0}{x}$ in its phase space Γ cannot be actually observed. If nothing at all is known about the position of $\overset{0}{x}$, it is possible only in quite exceptional cases to make any statement about the evolution of the system. Such an exceptional case is the system with the equations of motion

$$\dot{x}_\nu = -x_\nu, \quad \nu = 1, 2, \ldots, n.$$

Its general solution reads

$$x_\nu = \overset{\text{o}}{x}_\nu e^{-(t-\overset{\text{o}}{t})}, \quad \nu = 1, 2, ..., n.$$

It is seen immediately from this that, for any initial point $\overset{\text{o}}{x}$, the moving phase point $x = \chi(\overset{\text{o}}{x}, \overset{\text{o}}{t}, t)$ approaches the point O more and more closely in course of time. This kind of development is connected with the non-Hamiltonian character of the equations of motion (cf. § 11.3). Most mechanical systems, however, have Hamiltonian equations of motion so that this kind of evolution is not to be expected. (It may be mentioned that systems with the equations of motion

$$\dot{x}_\nu = +x_\nu, \quad \nu = 1, 2, ..., n$$

show just a contrary kind of development since in this case the general solution reads

$$x_\nu = \overset{\text{o}}{x}_\nu e^{(t-\overset{\text{o}}{t})}, \quad \nu = 1, 2, ..., n.)$$

Suppose, now, that the initial phase point of a given concrete system is not completely unknown, but is known to belong to a certain subset $\overset{\text{o}}{S}$ of Γ, say to a bounded set $\overset{\text{o}}{S}$. Then the moving phase point $\chi(\overset{\text{o}}{x}, \overset{\text{o}}{t}, t)$ is a point of the image $\chi(\overset{\text{o}}{S}, \overset{\text{o}}{t}, t)$ of the set $\overset{\text{o}}{S}$ at time t. By Theorems 5.7 and 11.1 also, $\chi(\overset{\text{o}}{S}, \overset{\text{o}}{t}, t)$ is bounded. If it were possible to determine $\chi(\overset{\text{o}}{S}, \overset{\text{o}}{t}, t)$, the statement that the moving phase point belongs to this set would, therefore, have some significance. So it seems useful to investigate the mapping $\chi(\overset{\text{o}}{S}, \overset{\text{o}}{t}, t)$.

11.1. THEOREM. *For fixed values of $\overset{\text{o}}{t}$ and t, the phase mapping $x = \chi(\overset{\text{o}}{x}, \overset{\text{o}}{t}, t)$ is topological. Its inverse mapping is given by $\overset{\text{o}}{x} = \chi(x, t, \overset{\text{o}}{t})$.*

For the proof, see §§ 10.1, 6.4, 10.3, 5.1.

11.2. THEOREM. *Let $\Delta(\overset{\text{o}}{x}, \overset{\text{o}}{t}, t)$ be the Jacobian determinant of the phase mapping $\chi(\overset{\text{o}}{x}, \overset{\text{o}}{t}, t)$ defined by*

$$\Delta(\overset{\text{o}}{x}, \overset{\text{o}}{t}, t) \equiv \det \left| \frac{\partial \chi_i(\overset{\text{o}}{x}, \overset{\text{o}}{t}, t)}{\partial \overset{\text{o}}{x}_j} \right|,$$

and $L = \chi(\overset{\text{o}}{L}, \overset{\text{o}}{t}, t)$ be the "phase image" of any Lebesgue subset $\overset{\text{o}}{L}$ of Γ. Then L is a Lebesgue set itself and

$$\mu L = \int_{\overset{\text{o}}{L}} \Delta(\overset{\text{o}}{x}, \overset{\text{o}}{t}, t)\, d\overset{\text{o}}{x}.$$

Proof. Assume that the statement has been demonstrated for Riemann-measurable sets, e.g. for bounded (open, half-open or closed) intervals. (See any textbook on integral calculus.) Then it is also valid for the sum of a finite or enumerable number of closed intervals which are meshes of a "network" (cf. § 4.5). Now apply it to such a sum which covers any given bounded Borel set B. By an obvious limiting process, it follows that

$$\mu B \geqslant \int_{\overset{\circ}{B}} \Delta(\overset{\circ}{x}, \overset{\circ}{t}|t) \, d\overset{\circ}{x}.$$

(The measurability of $\overset{\circ}{B} = \chi(B, t, \overset{\circ}{t})$ is guaranteed by Theorem 7.4.) Similarly, if J is a bounded interval containing B,

$$\mu(J - B) \geqslant \int_{\overset{\circ}{J} - \overset{\circ}{B}} \Delta(\overset{\circ}{x}, \overset{\circ}{t}, t) \, d\overset{\circ}{x}$$

(where J is the "original" of $\overset{\circ}{J}$). Now assume that

$$\mu B > \int_{\overset{\circ}{B}} \Delta(\overset{\circ}{x}, \overset{\circ}{t}, t) \, d\overset{\circ}{x}.$$

Then $$\mu J = \mu B + \mu(J - B) > \int_{\overset{\circ}{J}} \Delta(\overset{\circ}{x}, \overset{\circ}{t}, t) \, d\overset{\circ}{x},$$

which is a contradiction since J is a Riemann set. Hence

$$\mu B = \int_{\overset{\circ}{B}} \Delta(\overset{\circ}{x}, \overset{\circ}{t}, t) \, d\overset{\circ}{x}.$$

The extension to unbounded Borel sets is obvious.

Now let $\overset{\circ}{L}$ be any Lebesgue subset of Γ. Approximate $\overset{\circ}{L}$, according to Theorem 7.5, by two Borel sets $\overset{\circ}{A}$ and $\overset{\circ}{B}$ such that

$$\overset{\circ}{A} \subseteq \overset{\circ}{L} \subseteq \overset{\circ}{B}$$

and $$\mu \overset{\circ}{A} = \mu \overset{\circ}{L} = \mu \overset{\circ}{B}.$$

Then $$A \equiv \chi(\overset{\circ}{A}, \overset{\circ}{t}, t) \subseteq \chi(\overset{\circ}{L}, \overset{\circ}{t}, t) \subseteq \chi(\overset{\circ}{B}, \overset{\circ}{t}, t) \equiv B,$$

$$\mu A = \underline{\mu} A \leqslant \underline{\mu} L \leqslant \bar{\mu} L \leqslant \bar{\mu} B = \mu B.$$

Now, from $\mu A = \mu B$, it follows that $\underline{\mu} L = \bar{\mu} L$, and this implies the statement of the theorem.

11.3. THEOREM. *Denote the partial derivatives of the right-hand sides $X_i(x, t)$ of the equations of motion*

$$\dot{x}_i = X_i(x, t), \quad i = 1, 2, \ldots, n,$$

with respect to x_j by $X_{ij}(x, t)$, and denote the Jacobian Determinant $\det |\partial \chi_i(\overset{o}{x}, \overset{o}{t}, t)/\partial \overset{o}{x}_j|$ *of the solution functions $\chi_i(\overset{o}{x}, \overset{o}{t}, t)$ by* $\Delta(\overset{o}{x}, \overset{o}{t}, t)$. *Then*

$$\Delta(\overset{o}{x}, \overset{o}{t}, t) = \exp\left[\int_{\overset{o}{t}}^{t} \sum_{k=1}^{n} X_{kk}\{\chi(\overset{o}{x}, \overset{o}{t}, \tau), \tau\}\, d\tau\right]$$

for all values of $\overset{o}{x}, \overset{o}{t}, t$.

Proof. It will be shown that $\Delta(\overset{o}{x}, \overset{o}{t}, t)$ satisfies the ordinary differential equation $\partial \Delta / \partial t = \Delta \sum_{k=1}^{n} X_{kk}[\chi(\overset{o}{x}, \overset{o}{t}, t), t]$. From this equation and the initial condition that

$$\Delta(\overset{o}{x}, \overset{o}{t}, \overset{o}{t}) = \det\left|\frac{\partial \chi_i(\overset{o}{x}, \overset{o}{t}, \overset{o}{t})}{\partial \overset{o}{x}_j}\right| = \left|\frac{\partial \overset{o}{x}_i}{\partial \overset{o}{x}_j}\right| = 1,$$

the theorem follows immediately.

In order to derive the above differential equation, differentiate $\Delta(\overset{o}{x}, \overset{o}{t}, t)$ with respect to t. Thus:

$$\frac{\partial \Delta}{\partial t} = \begin{vmatrix} \dot{\chi}_{11}, & \dot{\chi}_{12}, & \cdots, & \dot{\chi}_{1n} \\ \chi_{21}, & \chi_{22}, & \cdots, & \chi_{2n} \\ \cdots & \cdots & \cdots & \cdots \\ \chi_{n1}, & \chi_{n2}, & \cdots, & \chi_{nn} \end{vmatrix} + \ldots$$

$$= \begin{vmatrix} \sum_j X_{1j}\chi_{j1}, & \sum_j X_{1j}\chi_{j2}, & \cdots, & \sum_j X_{1j}\chi_{jn} \\ \chi_{21}, & \chi_{22}, & \cdots, & \chi_{2n} \\ \cdots\cdots & \cdots\cdots & & \cdots\cdots \\ \chi_{n1}, & \chi_{n2}, & \cdots, & \chi_{nn} \end{vmatrix} + \ldots$$

(by Theorem 6.6)

$$= \sum_{j=1}^{n} X_{1j} \begin{vmatrix} \chi_{j1}, & \chi_{j2}, & \cdots, & \chi_{jn} \\ \chi_{21}, & \chi_{22}, & \cdots, & \chi_{2n} \\ \cdots & \cdots & \cdots & \cdots \\ \chi_{n1}, & \chi_{n2}, & \cdots, & \chi_{nn} \end{vmatrix} + \ldots$$

$$= (X_{11} \cdot \Delta + X_{12} \cdot 0 + \ldots + X_{1n} \cdot 0) + \ldots$$

$$= (X_{11} + X_{22} + \ldots + X_{nn}) \cdot \Delta. \qquad \text{Q.E.D.}$$

3

11.4. LIOUVILLE'S THEOREM (Corollary of Theorem 11.3). *If* $\sum\limits_{k=1} X_{kk}(x, t) \equiv 0$, *then* $\Delta(\overset{o}{x}, \overset{o}{l}, t) = 1$ *and* $\mu\chi(\overset{o}{L}, \overset{o}{l}, t) = \mu\overset{o}{L}$ *for all Lebesgue subsets* $\overset{o}{L}$ *of* R^n *and all values of* $\overset{o}{l}$ *and* t. *In particular, the phase mapping "conserves measure" for Hamiltonian equations of motion.*

Conversely, the conservation of measure implies that $\Delta(\overset{o}{x}, \overset{o}{l}, t) = 1$ and $\sum\limits_{k=1}^{n} X_{kk}(x, t) = 0$ for almost all values of $\overset{o}{x}$ or x, for fixed values of $\overset{o}{l}$ and t.

Both the following statements are also immediate consequences of Theorem 11.3. If

$$\sum_{k=1}^{n} X_{kk}(x, t) \geqslant \alpha$$

for all x and $t \geqslant \overset{o}{l}$, then

$$\Delta(\overset{o}{x}, \overset{o}{l}, t) \geqslant e^{\alpha(t - \overset{o}{l})}$$

for $t \geqslant \overset{o}{l}$; similarly, if

$$\sum_{k=1}^{n} X_{kk}(x, t) \leqslant \beta$$

for all x and $t \geqslant \overset{o}{l}$, then

$$0 \leqslant \Delta(\overset{o}{x}, \overset{o}{l}, t) \leqslant e^{\beta(t - \overset{o}{l})}$$

for $t \geqslant \overset{o}{l}$.

Notes. If the flow χ is considered as that of a substratum which flows in the phase space Γ, then Liouville's Theorem states: this substratum must be regarded as incompressible.

Further, the theorem admits the following interpretation. $\mu\overset{o}{L}$ can be considered as a measure for the uncertainty by which we know or describe the position of an initial point $\overset{o}{x}$ of a given concrete mechanical system. For Hamiltonian systems, the uncertainty μL of the moving phase-point $x = \chi(\overset{o}{x}, \overset{o}{l}, t)$ at any moment t, equals the uncertainty $\mu\overset{o}{L}$ of the initial point $\overset{o}{x}$. In the case of a non-Hamiltonian system, this uncertainty may change in course of time. (Cf. the example at the beginning of this section.) In particular, for systems with "frictional forces", $\Delta(\overset{o}{x}, \overset{o}{l}, t)$ and μL never increase, and in general decrease, in course of time, possibly towards the value 0.

For later use, the following consequence of Theorem 11.3 is given as an appendix.

11.5. THEOREM. *Let* $\Delta(\overset{\circ}{x}, \overset{?}{l}, t)$, *the Jacobian determinant of the phase mapping* $\chi(\overset{\circ}{x}, \overset{?}{l}, t)$, $\overset{\circ}{L}$ *be a Lebesgue subset of the phase space* Γ, $L = \chi(\overset{\circ}{L}, \overset{?}{l}, t)$ *its phase image at time* t, *and* $f(x)$ *a function which is integrable over* L. *Then* $f\{\chi(\overset{\circ}{x}, \overset{?}{l}, t)\}$ *is integrable over* $\overset{\circ}{L}$, *and*

$$\int_L f(x)\,\mathrm{d}x = \int_{\overset{\circ}{L}} f\{\chi(\overset{\circ}{x}, \overset{?}{l}, t)\} \cdot \Delta(\overset{\circ}{x}, \overset{?}{l}, t)\,\mathrm{d}\overset{\circ}{x}.$$

In particular, for measure-conserving phase mapping,

$$\int_L f(x)\,\mathrm{d}x = \int_{\overset{\circ}{L}} f\{\chi(\overset{\circ}{x}, \overset{?}{l}, t)\}\,\mathrm{d}\overset{\circ}{x}.$$

Outline of the proof. By Theorem 11.2, the statement holds for piecewise constant functions. From this, it follows immediately, by the Approximation Theorem 8.5, for bounded f and μL, and by Definitions 8.10, these restrictions can be dropped.

In the special case $\Delta \equiv 1$, the statement can be considered as an immediate consequence of the fact that for both integrals the sets of all Darboux sums coincide.

§ 12. Stationary measure-conserving phase flow; Poincaré's, Hopf's, and Jacobi's Theorems

12.1. DEFINITION. A subset J of the phase space Γ is said to be *invariant* (with respect to the phase flow χ) if

$$\chi(J, \overset{?}{l}, t) = J$$

for all values of $\overset{?}{l}$ and t.

Note. Obviously, a set J is invariant if and only if its characteristic function

$$\delta_J(x) = \begin{cases} 1, & \text{for} \quad x \in J, \\ 0, & \text{for} \quad x \in \Gamma - J, \end{cases}$$

is invariant.

12.2. POINCARÉ'S RECURRENCE THEOREM. *Let* J *be a subset of the phase space* Γ *of positive finite measure which is invariant with respect to the stationary measure-conserving phase flow* $x = \chi(\overset{\circ}{x}, t)$, *and let* τ *be any constant. Then almost every point* $\overset{\circ}{x}$ *of* J *is a limiting point of its sequence*

$$\overset{\circ}{x} = \chi(\overset{\circ}{x}, 0), \chi(\overset{\circ}{x}, \tau), \chi(\overset{\circ}{x}, 2\tau), \ldots.$$

Example. Let a vessel be divided into two equal parts by a sliding partition. Let one half be empty and the other contain a (monatomic) gas. If we pull the partition away, then the gas will, after a short time, fill the whole vessel uniformly, neglecting gravitational effects. The walls of the vessel can be mathematically represented by a potential of the following kind. Assume it to be equal to zero for all the points of the interior of the vessel whose distances ρ from the walls are larger than a suitable positive constant ρ_0. For distances $\rho \leqslant \rho_0$, define the potential by any monotonically decreasing function $\phi(\rho)$ which has a continuous derivative $\phi'(\rho)$ and for which

$$\left.\begin{array}{l} \phi(\rho_0) = 0, \\ \phi'(\rho_0) = 0. \end{array}\right\} \quad \lim_{\rho \to 0} \phi(\rho) = \infty.$$

The mutual repulsions which the particles exert on each other during collisions can be represented in a similar fashion. Then the particles form a system of mass-points whose equations of motion are Newtonian and whose potential does not depend on time. Hence the Recurrence Theorem applies. Therefore (if we neglect a set of possible initial points $\overset{\circ}{x}$ of vanishing measure), all the particles must collect in the half they occupied initially, again and again, even having approximately the same positions and velocities.

Proof. Let $B_{\delta,\lambda}$ be the set of all the points $\overset{\circ}{x}$ of J for which

$$|\chi(\overset{\circ}{x}, \lambda\tau) - \overset{\circ}{x}| > \delta,$$

where δ denotes any positive number and λ any positive integer. Put

$$B_\delta = \prod_{\lambda=1}^{\infty} B_{\delta,\lambda} \quad \text{and} \quad B = \sum_{d=1}^{\infty} B_{1/d}.$$

Then B is the set of all the points $\overset{\circ}{x}$ of J for which the statement of the theorem is not true. Its validity will be shown by the proof that $\mu B = 0$.

First, B is Lebesgue-measurable. For, since $\chi(\overset{\circ}{x}, \lambda\tau)$ is a continuous function of $\overset{\circ}{x}$ (cf. Theorem 6.4), $B_{\delta,\lambda}$ is open, by Theorem 5.3. Hence B_δ and B are Borel sets.

Denote the ϵ-neighbourhood of the point x by $U_\epsilon(x)$. Then, by Theorem 4.5, there is a finite or enumerable set of points

$a_1, a_2, \ldots$ of Γ such that

$$B_\delta \subseteq \sum_{i=1}^{\infty} U_\varepsilon(a_i)$$

and, therefore, $\qquad B_\delta = \sum_{i=1}^{\infty} B_\delta U_\varepsilon(a_i).$

Put $\qquad\qquad\qquad C_i = B_\delta U_\varepsilon(a_i).$

Then, secondly, all the sets $C_1, C_2, \ldots$ are Borel sets, and so they are Lebesgue-measurable.

Now suppose that any of the sets $C_1, C_2, \ldots$, say the set C_1, has a positive measure. Then there must be at least two of its images

$$C_1, \chi(C_1, \tau), \chi(C_1, 2\tau), \ldots$$

which have common points. For, otherwise,

$$\mu \sum_{\lambda=0}^{\infty} \chi(C_1, \lambda\tau) = \sum_{\lambda=0}^{\infty} \mu\chi(C_1, \lambda\tau) \qquad \text{(Theorem 7.3)}$$

$$= \sum_{\lambda=0}^{\infty} \mu C_1 \quad \text{(conservation of measure)}$$

$$= \infty,$$

while, at the same time,

$$\sum_{\lambda=0}^{\infty} \chi(C_1, \lambda\tau) \subseteq J$$

and, therefore, $\qquad \mu \sum_{\lambda=0}^{\infty} \chi(C_1, \lambda\tau) \leqslant \mu J < \infty$

(by the assumption of the theorem).

Thus the assumption that there are no images having common points leads to a contradiction.

Suppose that the sets $\chi(C_1, \lambda_1 \tau)$ and $\chi(C_1, \lambda_2 \tau)$ (where $0 \leqslant \lambda_1 < \lambda_2$) have common points. Denote them by C' and C''. Then, by 11.1, the sets $\chi(C', -\lambda_1 \tau)$ and $\chi(C'', -\lambda_1 \tau)$, i.e., by Theorem 10.3, the sets C_1 and $\chi(C_1, \overline{\lambda_2 - \lambda_1} \tau)$ also have a non-empty intersection C.

Let c be a point of C and

$$b = \chi(c, -\overline{\lambda_2 - \lambda_1} \tau) \quad \text{or} \quad c = \chi(b, \overline{\lambda_2 - \lambda_1} \tau).$$

Since b and c are points of C_1 and, therefore, of $U_\epsilon(a_1)$,

$$|c-b| \leqslant |c-a_1| + |a_1-b| < 2\epsilon < \delta$$

if ϵ is chosen $< \frac{1}{2}\delta$. On the other hand, the point b belongs to the set B_δ and, therefore, to the set $B_{\delta, \lambda_2-\lambda_1}$, for the points of which the inequality

$$|\chi(\overset{\circ}{x}, \overline{\lambda_2 - \lambda_1}\, \tau) - \overset{\circ}{x}| > \delta$$

holds. Hence, in particular,

$$|c-b| > \delta.$$

This contradicts the above result that $|c-b| < \delta$, and the contradiction can be made to disappear only by abandoning the assumption that $\mu B_\delta > 0$.

From $\mu B_\delta = 0$ it now follows that

$$\mu B = \mu \sum_{d=1}^{\infty} B_{1/d} \leqslant \sum_{d=1}^{\infty} \mu B_{1/d} = 0. \qquad \text{Q.E.D.}$$

12.3. FIRST THEOREM OF E. HOPF. *Let* $x = \chi(\overset{\circ}{x}, t)$ *be a stationary measure-conserving phase flow, and* τ *be an arbitrary constant. Then, for almost every point* $\overset{\circ}{x}$ *of the phase space* Γ, *either* $\overset{\circ}{x}$ *is a limiting point of the corresponding sequence*

$$\overset{\circ}{x} = \chi(\overset{\circ}{x}, 0),\ \chi(\overset{\circ}{x}, \tau),\ \chi(\overset{\circ}{x}, 2\tau),\ \dots,$$

or this sequence does not possess any limiting point at all, so that $|\chi(\overset{\circ}{x}, \lambda\tau)| \to \infty$ *if* $\lambda \to \infty$.

Proof. Let $A_{R,\lambda}$ be the set of all points $\overset{\circ}{x}$ of Γ for which

$$|\chi(\overset{\circ}{x}, \lambda\tau)| < R$$

where R and λ are any positive integers. Put

$$A_R = \prod_{\lambda=0}^{\infty} A_{R,\lambda}$$

and

$$A = \sum_{R=1}^{\infty} A_R.$$

Then A is the set of $\overset{\circ}{x}$ for which the sequence

$$|\overset{\circ}{x}|,\ |\chi(\overset{\circ}{x}, \tau)|,\ |\chi(\overset{\circ}{x}, 2\tau)|,\ \dots$$

is bounded. By Theorem 5.3, $A_{R,\lambda}$ is open; hence A_R and A are Borel sets.

Now denote by $B_{\delta,\lambda}$ the set of x for which

$$|\chi(\overset{\circ}{x},\lambda\tau) - \overset{\circ}{x}| > \delta.$$

In a way similar to § 12.2, put

$$B_\delta = \prod_{\lambda=1}^{\infty} B_{\delta,\lambda}$$

and

$$B = \sum_{d=1}^{\infty} B_{1/d}.$$

Then B is the set of all $\overset{\circ}{x}$ which are not limiting points of the corresponding sequences

$$\overset{\circ}{x},\ \chi(\overset{\circ}{x},\tau),\ \chi(\overset{\circ}{x},2\tau),\ \dots.$$

The set for which the alternative of the theorem does not apply is

$$AB = \sum_{R=1}^{\infty} A_R \sum_{d=1}^{\infty} B_{1/d}$$

$$= \sum_{R=1}^{\infty} \sum_{d=1}^{\infty} A_R B_{1/d}.$$

The sets $A_R B_{1/d}$ are, as Borel sets, Lebesgue-measurable. It is shown in a similar manner as in the proof of Theorem 12.2 that $\mu(A_R B_{1/d}) = 0$. Hence $\mu(AB) = 0$, and this is the statement of the theorem.

COROLLARY. If the right-hand sides of the equations of motion

$$\dot{x}_i = X_i(x),\quad i = 1, 2, \dots, n$$

satisfy the condition that

$$\sum_{k=1}^{n} \frac{\partial X_k(x)}{\partial x_k} \geqslant \alpha = \text{const.} > 0$$

for all points x of Γ, then, for $\tau > 0$ and almost all initial points $\overset{\circ}{x}$ of Γ,

$$\lim_{\lambda\to\infty} |\chi(\overset{\circ}{x},\lambda\tau)| = \infty.$$

If, however,

$$\sum_{k=1}^{\infty} \frac{\partial X_k(x)}{\partial x_k} \leqslant \alpha = \text{const.} < 0$$

for all points x of Γ, then, for any Lebesgue set $\overset{\circ}{L}$ of initial points $\overset{\circ}{x}$ of finite measure,

$$\lim_{\lambda\to\infty} \mu\chi(\overset{\circ}{L},\lambda\tau) = 0.$$

Proof of the case $\alpha > 0$:

$$\mu\chi(A_R, \lambda\tau) = \int_{\chi(A_R, \lambda\tau)} dx$$

$$= \int_{A_R} \Delta(\mathring{x}, \lambda\tau)\, d\mathring{x}$$

$$\geqslant e^{\alpha.\lambda\tau}.\mu A_R,$$

by the remarks following Theorem 11.4. Now, for all $\mathring{x}$ of A_R,

$$\chi(\mathring{x}, \nu\tau) \in U_R(0), \quad \nu = 0, 1, 2, \ldots$$

(by the definition of A_R), or,

$$\chi(A_R, \nu\tau) \subseteq U_R(0).$$

Hence $$e^{\alpha.\lambda\tau}\mu A_R \leqslant \mu\chi(A_R, \lambda\tau) \leqslant \mu U_R(0),$$

and this inequality can hold for all values of $\lambda = 0, 1, 2, \ldots$ only if $\mu A_R = 0$. Therefore $\mu A = 0$, too.   Q.E.D.

The proof of the case $\alpha < 0$ is similar.

12.4. SECOND THEOREM OF E. HOPF. *Let* $x = \chi(\mathring{x}, t)$ *be a stationary measure-conserving phase flow and* τ *any constant. Then almost every point* $\mathring{x}$ *of* Γ *which is a limiting point of the corresponding sequence*

$$\mathring{x} = \chi(\mathring{x}, 0),\ \chi(\mathring{x}, \tau),\ \chi(\mathring{x}, 2\tau),\ \ldots$$

is a limiting point of the sequence

$$\mathring{x},\ \chi(\mathring{x}, -\tau),\ \chi(\mathring{x}, -2\tau),\ \ldots$$

too, and for almost every point $\mathring{x}$ *for which*

$$\lim_{\lambda \to \infty} |\chi(\mathring{x}, \lambda\tau)| = \infty,$$

also $$\lim_{\lambda \to \infty} |\chi(\mathring{x}, -\lambda\tau)| = \infty.$$

The second part of the theorem is an immediate consequence of the first part and of Theorem 12.3, and vice versa. The essential content of the theorem is that the future and the past of the mechanical system under consideration are qualitatively similar for almost all initial points.

Proof. The symbols of §§ 12.2 and 12.3 are used with respect to the constant τ, and the same symbols with a dash denote the corresponding quantities related to the constant $(-\tau)$. If $\epsilon < \frac{1}{2}\delta$, no two sets of the sequence

$$D_i, \chi(D_i, \tau), \chi(D_i, 2\tau), \ldots$$

where $\quad D_i = U_\epsilon(a_i) B_\delta A_R', \quad i = 1, 2, 3, \ldots,$ fixed,

have common points. By successive mappings $\chi^{-1}, \chi^{-1}\chi^{-1}, \ldots$, it is seen that no two sets of the sequence

$$D_i, \chi(D_i, -\tau), (D_i, -2\tau), \ldots$$

have common points. Hence

$$\mu \sum_{\lambda=0}^{l} \chi(D_i, -\lambda\tau) = \sum_{\lambda=0}^{l} \mu\chi(D_i, -\lambda\tau) = (l+1).\mu D_i$$

for each positive integer l. Now

$$\chi(D_i, -\lambda\tau) \subseteq A_R' \subseteq U_R(0)$$

for each value of $\lambda = 0, 1, 2, \ldots$; therefore

$$\sum_{\lambda=0}^{l} \chi(D_i, -\lambda\tau) \subseteq U_R(0),$$

and, finally, $\quad \mu \sum_{\lambda=0}^{l} \chi(D_i, -\lambda\tau) \leqslant \mu U_R(0).$

Inserting the above value for the left-hand side yields

$$(l+1).\mu D_i \leqslant \mu U_R(0)$$

for $l = 0, 1, 2, \ldots$, which is possible only if $\mu D_i = 0$, i.e. $\mu\{B_\delta A_R' U_\epsilon(a_i)\} = 0$. Since

$$BA' = \sum_{d=1}^{\infty} B_{1/d} \sum_{R=1}^{\infty} A_R' \cdot \sum_{i=1}^{\infty} U_\epsilon(a_i)$$

$$= \sum_{i=1}^{\infty} \sum_{d=1}^{\infty} \sum_{R=1}^{\infty} B_{1/d} A_R' U_\epsilon(a_i)$$

and $\quad \mu\{B_{1/d} A_{R_1} U_\epsilon(a_i)\} = 0,$

it follows that $\mu(BA') = 0$. This implies the statement of the theorem because B contains all "points of divergence" with respect to τ and A' contains all limiting points with respect to $-\tau$.

12.5. As to the application of the previous theorems, the following *problems* arise:

(i) What are the necessary and sufficient conditions for recurrence and "flight" ($|x| \to \infty$)?

(ii) In the case of recurrence, how long is the period between the instant of starting from a given initial point $\hat{x}$ and that of the next recurrence?

(iii) How can the theorems be generalized to systems whose phase flows are not stationary or not measure-conserving?

It seems that little is known about the answers to these questions. In the following, a partial answer for question (i) will be given, which is a slight generalization of a theorem by Jacobi well known in Celestial Mechanics.

12.6. DEFINITION. A function $V(q)$, $q = (q_1, ..., q_n)$, which is defined in R^n is said to be *homogeneous* in q of order α if, for any real number λ,

$$V(\lambda q) \equiv \lambda^\alpha V(q).$$

12.7. EULER'S IDENTITY. Let the function $V(q)$, defined in R^n, be homogeneous in q of order α and possess derivatives with respect to $q_1, q_2, ..., q_n$. Then

$$\sum_{\nu=1}^{n} q_\nu \frac{\partial V(q)}{\partial q_\nu} \equiv \alpha V(q).$$

Proof. Differentiate the identity which defines a homogeneous function with respect to λ for $\lambda = 1$.

12.8. LAGRANGE'S IDENTITY. *Let*

$$\left. \begin{array}{l} m\dot{q}_\nu = p_\nu \\ \dot{p}_\nu = -V_\nu(q,t) \end{array} \right\}, \quad \nu = 1, ..., n$$

be the equations of motion of a system of n mass-points (cf. § 10.4). Here $V_\nu(q,t)$ denotes the derivative $(\partial/\partial q_\nu) V(q,t)$ of a potential function $V(q,t)$ which is assumed to be homogeneous in q of order α. Then, for each solution (p,q) of the equations of motion,

$$\frac{d^2}{dt^2} \left(\frac{1}{2} \sum_{\nu=1}^{n} m_\nu q_\nu^2 \right) \equiv 2L - \alpha V(q,t),$$

where L is the kinetic energy $\dfrac{1}{2} \sum_{\nu=1}^{n} \dfrac{p_\nu^2}{m_\nu}$ of the system.

Proof.

$$\frac{d}{dt}\left(\frac{1}{2}\sum_1^n m_\nu q_\nu^2\right) \equiv \sum_1^n m_\nu q_\nu \dot{q}_\nu,$$

$$\frac{d^2}{dt^2}\left(\frac{1}{2}\sum_1^n m_\nu q_\nu^2\right) \equiv \sum_1^n m_\nu \dot{q}_\nu^2 + \sum_1^n q_\nu . m_\nu \ddot{q}_\nu$$

$$\equiv \sum_1^n \frac{p_\nu^2}{m_\nu} - \sum_1^n q_\nu . V_\nu$$

(by the equations of motion),

$$\equiv 2L - \alpha V$$

(by Euler's Lemma 12.7).

Q.E.D.

12.9. JACOBI'S THEOREM. *Let the potential function $V(q)$ of a system of mass-points be independent of the time variable t and be homogeneous in q of order α, where $-2 \leqslant \alpha \leqslant 0$. Then, if the total energy of the system,*

$$E = L + V(q),$$

is non-negative, there are two constants A and B such that

$$\frac{1}{2}\sum_{\nu=1}^n m_\nu q_\nu^2 \geqslant A + Bt + \tfrac{1}{2}|\alpha| Et^2$$

for $t \geqslant 0$. If $\alpha = -2$,

$$\frac{1}{2}\sum_1^n m_\nu q_\nu^2 = A + Bt + Et^2.$$

Proof. Eliminating $V(q)$ from Lagrange's Identity 12.8 and the energy equation $E = L + V(q)$ yields

$$\left(\frac{1}{2}\sum_1^n m_\nu q_\nu^2\right)^{..} = (2 + \alpha)L - \alpha E,$$

which implies the statement of the theorem.

Necessary conditions for $\lim\limits_{t \to \infty}|q| = \infty$ are not known, except in a few special cases.

§ 13. The theorems of v. Neumann and Birkhoff; the ergodic hypothesis

Poincaré's and Hopf's theorems were obtained by embedding the single systems under consideration into appropriate ensembles of systems or, more properly, by embedding the single initial points into sets of such points. A second, additional method of characterizing the evolution of mechanical systems consists in the use of the time averages of any interesting functions $f(x)$ defined in the phase space Γ. Such time averages are obtained by replacing the independent variable x of the function $f(x)$ by the moving phase-point $\chi(\mathring{x}, t)$ and then averaging over time.

13.1. DEFINITION. Let $x = \chi(\mathring{x}, t)$ be a stationary measure-conserving phase flow (for which $\chi(\mathring{x}, 0) \equiv \mathring{x}$) and $f(x)$ be a function which is defined in the phase space Γ and integrable over each Lebesgue subset of Γ of finite measure. Then the expression

$$\hat{f}(\mathring{x}, t) \equiv \frac{1}{t} \int_0^t f\{\chi(\mathring{x}, t)\} \, \mathrm{d}t$$

is called the *time average* of the function $f(x)$ for the initial point $\mathring{x}$, provided that the integral on the right-hand side exists.

13.2. THEOREM. *For any value of t, the time average $\hat{f}(\mathring{x}, t)$ exists for almost all initial points $\mathring{x}$ and is integrable over each Lebesgue subset of Γ of finite measure.*

Proof. Let $\mathring{L}$ be a Lebesgue subset of Γ of finite measure and $L = \chi(\mathring{L}, t)$ its image at time t. Then, since

$$\int_{\mathring{L}} f\{\chi(\mathring{x}, t)\} \, \mathrm{d}\mathring{x} = \int_L f(x) \, \mathrm{d}x$$

(by Theorem 11.5), the integral on the left-hand side of this equation is a continuous function of t and, therefore, integrable with respect to t. Hence, by Theorem 8.16, the statement of the theorem follows for almost all points of $\mathring{L}$. For its extension to the whole space Γ, cover Γ by an enumerable number of Lebesgue sets of finite measure.

13.3. J. VON NEUMANN'S FIRST THEOREM. *Let $x = \chi(\mathring{x}, t)$ be a stationary measure-conserving phase flow, τ be an arbitrary* *constant and $f(x)$ be a function which is Lebesgue-measurable in the phase space Γ and the square of which is integrable over Γ. Then there is a function $f^*(\overset{0}{x})$ of the same kind such that*

$$\lim_{l\to\infty} \int_\Gamma \left| \frac{1}{l}\sum_{\lambda=0}^{l-1} f\{\chi(\overset{0}{x},\lambda\tau)\} - f^*(\overset{0}{x}) \right|^2 d\overset{0}{x} = 0.$$

Proof. Let R be the set of all the functions $\phi(x)$ which are measurable in Γ and of which the squares are integrable over Γ, and make R a Hilbert space by defining a product (g,h) of any two of its elements by $(g,h) = \int_\Gamma g(x)h(x)\,dx$ (cf. § 9). If $\phi(x)\in R$, then $\phi\{\chi(\overset{0}{x},t)\}\in R$, too. (The proof is similar to that of Theorem 13.2.) Now let L be the linear subset of R which consists of all elements of R having the form $\phi\{\chi(\overset{0}{x},t)\}-\phi(\overset{0}{x})$. First, the theorem will be proved for the elements f of L.

Introducing such abbreviations as f_λ for $f\{\chi(\overset{0}{x},\lambda\tau)\}$, we obtain

$$\left\| \frac{1}{l}\sum_{\lambda=0}^{l-1} f_\lambda \right\| = \left\| \frac{1}{l}\sum_{\lambda=0}^{l-1}(\phi_{\lambda+1}-\phi_\lambda) \right\|$$

$$= \left\| \frac{1}{l}(\phi_l-\phi_0) \right\|$$

$$\leqslant \frac{1}{l}(\|\phi_l\|+\|\phi_0\|) \qquad \text{(by § 9.2)}$$

$$= \frac{2}{l}\|\phi\|. \qquad \text{(by § 11.5)}$$

Hence
$$\lim_{l\to\infty}\left\| \frac{1}{c}\sum_0^{l-1} f_\lambda \right\| = 0.$$

The same relation holds for each limiting element f' of L. For, if $f\in L$,

$$\left\| \frac{1}{l}\sum_{\lambda=0}^{l-1} f'_\lambda \right\| \leqslant \left\| \frac{1}{l}\sum_0^{l-1} f_\lambda \right\| + \left\| \frac{1}{l}\sum_0^{l-1}(f'_\lambda-f_\lambda) \right\|$$

$$\leqslant \frac{2}{l}\|\phi\|+\|f'-f\| \qquad \text{(by Theorem 11.5)},$$

and the right-hand side is, for sufficiently large l and sufficiently small $\|f'-f\|$, arbitrarily small.

Now let $\bar{L}$ be the linear subspace belonging to L (cf. § 9.4) and f be any element of R. By Theorem 9.5,

$$f = g + h$$

where g is an element of $\bar{L}$ and h orthogonal to each element of $\bar{L}$. Hence

$$(h, \phi_\lambda - \phi) = 0$$

for each element ϕ of R (since $\phi_\lambda - \phi \in \bar{L}$), or

$$(h, \phi_\lambda) - (h, \phi) = 0.$$

Since
$$(h, \phi_\lambda) = (h_{-\lambda}, \phi),$$

by Theorem 11.5,

$$(h_{-\lambda}, \phi) - (h, \phi) = 0$$

or
$$(h_{-\lambda} - h, \phi) = 0.$$

In particular, for $\phi = h_{-\lambda} - h$,

$$(h_{-\lambda} - h, h_{-\lambda} - h) = 0,$$

i.e.
$$h_{-\lambda} - h = 0$$

or
$$h = h_\lambda.$$

Therefore,
$$\left\| \frac{1}{l} \sum_0^{l-1} f_\lambda - h \right\| = \left\| \frac{1}{l} \sum_0^{l-1} (f_\lambda - h_\lambda) \right\|$$

$$\leqslant \left\| \frac{1}{l} \sum_0^{l-1} g_\lambda \right\|,$$

and finally, since $g \in \bar{L}$,

$$\lim_{l \to \infty} \left\| \frac{1}{l} \sum_0^{l-1} f_\lambda - h \right\| = 0,$$

that is,
$$f^* = h,$$

or, by Theorem 9.3, $\quad f^*(x) = h(x)$

for almost all points x of Γ. Q.E.D.

13.4. J. VON NEUMANN'S SECOND THEOREM. *Let $x = \chi(\overset{\circ}{x}, t)$ be a stationary measure-conserving phase flow and $f(x)$ be a function which is Lebesgue-measurable in the phase space Γ and the square of which is integrable over Γ. Then there is a function $\hat{f}_\infty(\overset{\circ}{x})$ of the same kind such that*

$$\lim_{t \to \infty} \int_\Gamma \{\hat{f}(\overset{\circ}{x}, t) - \hat{f}_\infty(\overset{\circ}{x})\}^2 \, d\overset{\circ}{x} = 0$$

where $\hat{f}(\overset{0}{x}, t)$ denotes the time average

$$\frac{1}{t} \int_0^t f\{\chi(\overset{0}{x}, s)\}\,ds$$

of $f(x)$. The function $\hat{f}_\infty(\overset{0}{x})$ is invariant with respect to the phase flow χ.

Proof. Let T be any positive constant and l the largest integer $\leqslant T$. Then, by the Triangular Inequality 9.2,

$$\left\| \frac{1}{T} \int_0^T f\{\chi(\overset{0}{x}, t)\}\,dt \right\| \leqslant \frac{1}{T} \left\| \int_0^l f\{\chi(\overset{0}{x}, t)\}\,dt \right\| + \frac{1}{T} \left\| \int_l^T f\{\chi(\overset{0}{x}, t)\}\,dt \right\|. \quad (*)$$

Now, for any two positive constants α and β such that $\alpha < \beta$,

$$\left\| \int_\alpha^\beta f\{\chi(\overset{0}{x}, t)\}\,dt \right\|^2 = \int_\Gamma \left\{ \int_\alpha^\beta f[\chi(\overset{0}{x}, t)]\,dt \cdot \int_\alpha^\beta f[\chi(\overset{0}{x}, s)]\,ds \right\} d\overset{0}{x}$$

$$= \int_\alpha^\beta \int_\alpha^\beta \left\{ \int_\Gamma f[\chi(\overset{0}{x}, t)] f[\chi(\overset{0}{x}, s)]\,d\overset{0}{x} \right\} dt\,ds$$

(by Theorem 11.2 and Fubini's Theorem 8.15),

$$\leqslant \int_\alpha^\beta \int_\alpha^\beta \left\{ \int_\Gamma f^2[\chi(\overset{0}{x}, t)]\,d\overset{0}{x} \cdot \int_\Gamma f^2[\chi(\overset{0}{x}, s)]\,d\overset{0}{x} \right\}^{\frac{1}{2}} dt\,ds$$

(by Schwarz' inequality 9.2)

$$= \int_\alpha^\beta \int_\alpha^\beta \|f\|^2\,ds\,dt \quad \text{(by Theorem 11.5)},$$

or, $$\left\| \int_\alpha^\beta f[\chi(\overset{0}{x}, t)]\,dt \right\|^2 \leqslant (\beta - \alpha)^2 \|f\|^2. \quad (**)$$

Hence $$\frac{1}{T} \left\| \int_l^T f[\chi(\overset{0}{x}, t)]\,dt \right\| \leqslant \frac{T-l}{T} \|f\| < \frac{1}{T} \|f\|,$$

so that the last term of equation (*) tends towards zero if $t \to \infty$. So, for the proof of the theorem, it is only necessary to show that

$$\frac{1}{T} \int_0^l f[\chi(\overset{0}{x}, t)]\,dt \quad \text{or} \quad \frac{l}{T} \cdot \frac{1}{l} \int_0^l f[\chi(\overset{0}{x}, t)]\,dt$$

converges (as an element of the Hilbert space R) towards a limiting element $\hat{f}_\infty$.

For this, define functions (or elements of R) f_λ by

$$f_\lambda = \int_\lambda^{\lambda+1} f\{\chi(\overset{\circ}{x}, t)\}\, \mathrm{d}t = \int_0^1 f\{\chi(\overset{\circ}{x}, \lambda+s)\}\, \mathrm{d}s.$$

(Note that these f_λ's are different from those in the proof of Theorem 13.3.) Then

$$\frac{1}{l}\int_0^l f\{\chi(\overset{\circ}{x}, t)\}\, \mathrm{d}t = \frac{1}{l}\sum_{\lambda=0}^{l-1} f_\lambda,$$

and $\|f_\lambda\| \leqslant \|f\|$, by the inequality (**). The proof that

$$\frac{1}{l}\sum_{\lambda=0}^{l-1} f_\lambda$$

converges towards a limiting element $\hat{f}_\infty$ is analogous to that of Theorem 13.3.

Now we must demonstrate the invariance of $\hat{f}_\infty$. We have

$$\left\| \frac{1}{T}\int_0^T f\{\chi(\overset{\circ}{x}, s)\}\, \mathrm{d}s - \frac{1}{T}\int_0^T f\{\chi[\chi(\overset{\circ}{x}, t), s]\}\, \mathrm{d}s \right\|$$

$$= \frac{1}{T}\left\| \int_0^T f\{\chi(\overset{\circ}{x}, s)\}\, \mathrm{d}s - \int_0^T f\{\chi(\overset{\circ}{x}, t+s)\}\, \mathrm{d}s \right\|$$

$$\text{(by Theorem 10.3),}$$

$$= \frac{1}{T}\left\| \int_0^T f\{\chi(\overset{\circ}{x}, s)\}\, \mathrm{d}s - \int_t^{T+t} f\{\chi(\overset{\circ}{x}, s)\}\, \mathrm{d}s \right\|$$

$$= \frac{1}{T}\left\| \int_0^t + \int_t^T - \int_t^T - \int_T^{T+t} \right\|$$

$$\leqslant \frac{1}{T}\left\| \int_0^t \right\| + \frac{1}{T}\left\| \int_T^{T+t} \right\|$$

$$\text{(by the Triangular Inequality 9.2),}$$

$$\leqslant 2\frac{t}{T}\|f\| \qquad \text{(by inequality **).}$$

By letting $T \to \infty$, it follows that

$$\hat{f}_\infty(\overset{\circ}{x}) = \hat{f}_\infty\{\chi(\overset{\circ}{x}, t)\}$$

for almost all $\overset{\circ}{x}$ of Γ.

$$\text{Q.E.D.}$$

13.5. Under more restricted assumptions, more specialized statements can be made, namely:

BIRKHOFF'S THEOREMS. *Assume that for the stationary measure-conserving phase flow* $x = \chi(\overset{o}{x}, t)$, *there is an invariant subset J of Γ of (positive) finite measure. Further, let τ be a constant and $f(x)$ a function which is integrable over J. Then the sequence*

$$\frac{1}{l} \sum_{\lambda=0}^{l-1} f\{\chi(\overset{o}{x}, \lambda\tau)\}$$

converges for almost all points $\overset{o}{x}$ of J if $l \to \infty$. The limit function is integrable over J.

Under the same assumptions, *the time average $\hat{f}(\overset{o}{x}, t)$ converges for almost all points $\overset{o}{x}$ of J towards a function $\hat{f}_\infty(\overset{o}{x})$ which is integrable over J. The function $\hat{f}_\infty(\overset{o}{x})$ is invariant with respect to the phase flow χ.*

OUTLINE OF THE PROOF OF THE FIRST THEOREM. According to §§ 8.5, 8.10 and 8.11, the function $f(x)$ can be approximated by a piecewise constant function

$$c_0(x) = \sum_{\nu} \alpha_{0\nu} \delta_{L_{0\nu}}(x), \quad x \in J,$$

where the α's are constants, δ denotes characteristic functions and the L's are Lebesgue subsets of J. Therefore it is sufficient to demonstrate the theorem for such a function. Denote the sequence considered in the theorem by $c_0(x), c_1(x), c_2(x), \ldots$. All its terms are piecewise constant functions also:

$$c_\lambda(x) = \sum_{\nu} \alpha_{\lambda\nu} \delta_{L_{\lambda\nu}}(x), \quad \lambda = 0, 1, 2, \ldots .$$

Now let L^κ be the set of all the points of J which are contained in exactly κ sets $L_{\lambda\nu}$, where $\lambda = 0, 1, 2, \ldots, \nu = 1, 2, \ldots$. Thus,

$$J = L^1 + L^2 + \ldots$$

and no two of the sets $L^1, L^2, \ldots$ have common points. The aggregate $\{L^1, L^2, \ldots\}$ is enumerable. Thus,

$$c_\lambda(x) = \sum_{\nu} \beta_{\lambda\nu} \delta_{L^\nu}(x), \quad \beta_{\lambda\nu} = \text{const.}$$

Denote the lower and upper limits of the sequences

$$\{\beta_{0\nu}, \beta_{1\nu}, \beta_{2\nu}, \ldots\}$$

by $\underline{\beta}_\nu$ and $\bar{\beta}_\nu$, let $\{\beta_{\lambda_1'\nu}, \beta_{\lambda_2'\nu}, \beta_{\lambda_3'\nu}, \ldots\}$ and $\{\beta_{\lambda_1''\nu}, \beta_{\lambda_2''\nu}, \beta_{\lambda_3''\nu}, \ldots\}$ be sub-sequences which tend towards $\underline{\beta}_\nu$ and $\bar{\beta}_\nu$, respectively, and put

$$\underline{c}(x) = \sum_\nu \underline{\beta}_\nu \,\delta_{L^\nu}(x), \quad \bar{c}(x) = \sum_\nu \bar{\beta}_\nu \,\delta_{L^\nu}(x).$$

Then $\quad 0 \leqslant \displaystyle\int_{L^\nu} \{\bar{c}(x) - \underline{c}(x)\}\,\mathrm{d}x = (\bar{\beta}_\nu - \underline{\beta}_\nu)\,\mu L^\nu$

$$= (\bar{\beta}_\nu - \beta_{\lambda_{\kappa''}\nu})\,\mu L^\nu + (\beta_{\lambda_{\kappa''}\nu} - \beta_{\lambda_{\iota'}\nu})\,\mu L^\nu + (\beta_{\lambda_{\iota'}\nu} - \underline{\beta}_\nu)\,\mu L^\nu.$$

The first and third terms of the right-hand side tend towards zero if $\iota \to \infty, \kappa \to \infty$. The same holds for the second term also; for,

$$0 \leqslant (\beta_{\lambda_{\kappa''}\nu} - \beta_{\lambda_{\iota'}\nu})^2 \,\mu L^\nu = \int_{L^\nu} \{c_{\lambda_{\kappa''}}(x) - c_{\lambda_{\iota'}}(x)\}^2\,\mathrm{d}x$$

$$\leqslant \int_J \{c_{\lambda_{\kappa''}}(x) - c_{\lambda_{\iota'}}(x)\}^2\,\mathrm{d}x,$$

and the right-hand side tends towards zero because of v. Neumann's First Theorem 13.3. Hence $\bar{c} - \underline{c}$ can be positive only on a subset of J of measure zero, and this proves the theorem.

The second theorem can be demonstrated in a similar fashion.

Note and Corollary. Let L be a Lebesgue subset of Γ and $\delta_L(x)$ be its characteristic function. Then the mean value

$$\frac{1}{l} \sum_{\lambda=0}^{l-1} \delta_L\{\chi(\overset{\circ}{x}, \lambda\tau)\}$$

is the fractional number of all those points of the finite sequence $\chi(\overset{\circ}{x}, 0), \chi(\overset{\circ}{x}, \tau), \ldots, \chi(\overset{\circ}{x}, \overline{l-1}\,\tau)$ which belong to L. Similarly, the time average $\hat{\delta}_L(\overset{\circ}{x}, t)$ gives that fraction of the time interval $0 \ldots t$ during which the moving phase point $\chi(\overset{\circ}{x}, s), 0 \leqslant s \leqslant t$ belongs to L. It is called the *relative period* (*relativ Verweilzeit*) of the moving phase point in L (for the initial point $\overset{\circ}{x}$ during the interval $0 \ldots t$). For this, Birkhoff's Second Theorem asserts that, *for almost all points $\overset{\circ}{x}$ of an invariant subset J of finite measure, there is a limit towards which the relative period $\hat{\delta}_L(\overset{\circ}{x}, t)$ tends if $t \to \infty$.*

13.6. Boltzmann assumed that, for the initial points $\overset{\circ}{x}$ of an invariant subset J of positive finite measure, the limit $\hat{f}_\infty(\overset{\circ}{x})$ of the time average $\hat{f}(\overset{\circ}{x}, t)$ of any "*phase function*" $f(x)$ coincides with its *phase average* $\bar{f}$ defined by

$$\bar{f} = \frac{\displaystyle\int_J f(x)\,\mathrm{d}x}{\displaystyle\int_J \mathrm{d}x} = \frac{\displaystyle\int_J f(x)\,\mathrm{d}x}{\mu J}.$$

This assumption (or, rather, variations of it—see below) is called the *ergodic hypothesis*. Applied to the characteristic function of any Lebesgue subset L of J, it states that the limit $\overset{\mathrm{S}}{\delta}_{L\infty}(\overset{\mathrm{0}}{x})$ of the relative period of L is given by $\delta_L = \mu L/\mu J$ for (almost) all points $\overset{\mathrm{0}}{x}$ of J. This fraction is sometimes called the "probability" that the initial point $\overset{\mathrm{0}}{x}$ belongs to L (cf. §§ 14 and 15).

In this form, however, the supposition cannot be generally true. If, for example, the mechanical system under consideration is Hamiltonian, then its Hamiltonian function $H(x)$ is an invariant function (by § 10.5) so that $\hat{H}_\infty(\overset{\mathrm{0}}{x}) = \hat{H}(\overset{\mathrm{0}}{x}, t) = H(\overset{\mathrm{0}}{x})$. But, in general, $H(\overset{\mathrm{0}}{x}) \neq \bar{H}$.

This difficulty is apparently removed by taking the "surface" $H(x) = E \equiv \mathrm{const.}$ of the $2n$-dimensional phase space Γ as the invariant subset J, introducing an invariant $(2n-1)$-dimensional measure on it (which is possible) and defining the phase average by means of the new measure (as, in fact, Boltzmann did). This procedure can also be interpreted in the following fashion. At first, for any positive value of ΔE, the set of all points x of Γ for which $E \leqslant H(x) \leqslant E + \Delta E$ is taken as the invariant subset J, and then $\Delta E \to 0$. If several First Integrals are known, a corresponding number of similar reductions can be made.

Suppose, for simplicity, that only the energy integral is known. Are, then, the phase average and the limit of the time average equal for the points of the surface $H(x) = E$? Boltzmann supposed that, in course of time, the moving phase point passes through all the points of the invariant set, and from this he inferred that both averages should be equal. But unfortunately the assumption is wrong, for topological reasons, and in any case the conclusion would require a more rigorous proof.

Now we shall give a necessary and sufficient condition for the truth of the ergodic hypothesis, which is due to Birkhoff.

For simplicity, the theorem and its proof will be formulated only for invariant subsets of the n-dimensional phase space Γ of positive finite n-dimensional measure, although both the theorem and the proof remain essentially valid for invariant subsets which are obtained by reduction by means of known First Integrals. First, a definition is to be given.

13.7. Definition. Let J be a Lebesgue-measurable subset of the phase space Γ of positive measure which is invariant with respect to the stationary measure-conserving phase flow $x = \chi(\overset{0}{x}, t)$. If, then, J contains an invariant subset J_1 such that $\mu J_1 > 0$ and $\mu(J - J_1) > 0$, the set J is said to be *metrically decomposible*.

13.8. Theorem of Birkhoff. *Let there be an invariant subset J of positive finite measure for the stationary measure-conserving phase flow χ which is metrically not decomposible, and let $f(x)$ be a function which is integrable over J. Then, for almost all points $\overset{0}{x}$ of J, the limit $\hat{f}_\infty(\overset{0}{x})$ of the time average $\hat{f}(\overset{0}{x}, t)$ equals the phase average $\bar{f}$. Conversely, if J is an invariant subset of positive finite measure and if, for each function $f(x)$ which is integrable over J, $\hat{f}_\infty(x) = \bar{f}$ for almost all points $\overset{0}{x}$ of J, then J is metrically not decomposible.*

We first prove the second part of the theorem. Suppose that, contrary to its statement, J is metrically decomposible into the two subsets J_1 and $J - J_1$ of positive measures. Then, for the characteristic function $\delta_{J_1}(x)$ of J_1,

$$0 < \bar{\delta}_{J_1} = \frac{\mu J_1}{\mu J} < 1$$

and
$$\delta_{J_1 \infty}(\overset{0}{x}) = \delta_{J_1}(\overset{0}{x}) \neq \bar{\delta}_{J_1}.$$

Hence the assumption of the proof is wrong, and the second statement of the theorem is correct.

As to its first part, suppose that the function $\hat{f}_\infty(\overset{0}{x})$ is not constant almost everywhere in J. Then there is a constant c and a set J_1 such that

$$\hat{f}_\infty(\overset{0}{x}) \leqslant c \quad \text{if} \quad \overset{0}{x} \in J_1 \subset J,$$
$$\hat{f}_\infty(\overset{0}{x}) > c \quad \text{if} \quad \overset{0}{x} \in J - J_1,$$

where (by Theorem 8.4) J_1 and $J - J_1$ are measurable sets and, by the assumption of the (indirect) proof,

$$\mu J_1 > 0, \quad \mu(J - J_1) > 0.$$

Since, by Theorem 13.4, the function $\hat{f}_\infty(\overset{0}{x})$ is invariant, the sets J_1 and $J - J_1$ are invariant, too. This contradicts the assumption of the theorem that J is metrically not decomposible. Hence the assumption of the proof is wrong, i.e. the function $\hat{f}_\infty(\overset{0}{x})$ is constant almost everywhere in J, say $\hat{f}_\infty(\overset{0}{x}) = C$ for almost all $\overset{0}{x}$ of J.

Therefore, $\qquad\qquad \hat{f}_\infty(\overset{0}{x}) = C.$

Now $\qquad\qquad\qquad \bar{\hat{f}} = \hat{\bar{f}} = \bar{f},$

for all values of t. (This is fairly obvious. The detailed proof will be given in § 19.10.) Hence, by letting $t \to \infty$,

$$\bar{f} = C = \hat{f}_\infty(x)$$

for almost all $\overset{0}{x}$ of J. $\qquad\qquad\qquad\qquad$ Q.E.D.

Note. A further question now is: Under what conditions is there, for a given stationary measure-conserving phase flow, an invariant subset of finite positive measure which is metrically not decomposible? It seems that a sufficiently general solution of this extremely difficult problem has not yet been found. Suppose that an invariant set J of positive finite measure is known. By 13.7 the set J is certainly metrically decomposible if we know a (continuous) First Integral of the equations of motion which is not constant in J. But what about the case when such an integral is not known? This does not imply at all that there is none. And it is just this case which nearly always occurs in applications of the theory, at least after a few reductions by the known invariant functions (if these reductions are practicable at all).

The merit of Birkhoff's Theorem is that it eliminates the function $f(x)$ from the investigation. Thus it shows that "ergodicity" is a property of the phase flow χ alone. But any further step into this direction appears to be hindered by insurmountable difficulties.

So the vindication of the ergodic hypothesis or, rather, of a substitute of it, will be attempted in another way. An important tool will be the concept of probability, which already has been mentioned in § 13.6. It will be developed in the next chapter.

References

The author has expounded his views on the nature of axioms in more detail in the following essay:

[16] KURTH, R., Wesen und Wert mathematischer Wahrheit. *Philosophia Naturalis*, **5**, pp. 129–173, 1958.

Presumably, Hamel's axiomatics of classical mechanics is to be understood in Hilbert's sense:

[17] HAMEL, G., Die Axiome der Mechanik, *Handb. Physik*, Vol. V.

References to Hamel's original papers on this subject are found there.

As to the theorems of Poincaré, Hopf, v. Neumann, Birkhoff, and the problems connected with them, see

[18] HOPF, E., *Ergodentheorie*, Berlin, 1937.

There, also, further references can be found. Some of the original papers make somewhat easier reading than Hopf's very concise summarizing report. See, for example,

[19] CARATHÉODORY, C., Über den Wiederkehrsatz von Poincaré, *Sitzungsber. Preuss. Akad. Wiss.*, p. 586, 1919.

[20] HOPF, E., Zwei Sätze uber den wahrscheinlichen Verlauf der Bewegungen dynamischer Systems, *Math. Ann.*, **103**, p. 710, 1938.

[21] NEUMANN, J. v., Proof of the quasiergodic hypothesis, *Proc. Nat. Acad. U.S.A.*, **18**, p. 70, 1932.

In the same volume there is Birkhoff's original paper:

[22] BIRKHOFF, G. D., Proof of the ergodic theorem, *Proc. Nat. Acad. U.S.A.*, **18**, p. 650, 1932.

Another presentation of this proof is given by

[23] KHINCHIN, A. J., *Mathematical Foundations of Statistical Mechanics*, New York, 1949.

In this book, excellent by virtue of its clarity and concentration upon the fundamentals, a detailed discussion of the ergodic problem is also given.

Boltzmann summarized his contributions to statistical mechanics in his book:

[24] BOLTZMANN, L., *Vorlesungen über Gastheorie*, two volumes, Leipzig, 1896–98.

Many of Boltzmann's arguments have been repeated by "almost all" textbooks and, I am sorry to add, not always in a critical fashion. A comprehensive and convenient survey over the literature, development and present aspect of conventional statistical mechanics has recently been given by

[25] TER HAAR, D., Foundations of Statistical Mechanics, *Rev. Mod. Phys.*, **27**, pp. 289–338, 1955.

CHAPTER IV

THE INITIAL DISTRIBUTION OF
PROBABILITY IN THE PHASE SPACE

§ 14. A formal description of the concept of probability

In § 12 it was assumed that the initial phase point $\overset{\circ}{x}$ of a given mechanical system was known to belong to a certain proper subset $\overset{\circ}{B}$ of the phase space Γ. Actually, in general, very much less is known; namely, only that $\overset{\circ}{x}$ belongs to $\overset{\circ}{B}$ "with a certain probability". What is meant by the word "probability" can be made (more or less) clear, according to Gibbs, by the following mental construction. Consider a *fictitious ensemble* of a large number of mechanical systems which are equal to the given one. "Equal" means that all these systems are governed by the same equations of motion, but have, in general, different initial points $\overset{\circ}{x}$. Then the probability that the initial point of the system actually given belongs to the subset $\overset{\circ}{B}$ of Γ is identified with the frequency of all those systems of the fictitious ensemble whose initial points $\overset{\circ}{x}$ lie in $\overset{\circ}{B}$. "Frequency" means the number of systems having initial points in $\overset{\circ}{B}$, divided by the number of all the systems of the ensemble.

A restriction, however, is to be made. If there are N systems in the ensemble, the frequency belonging to any set $\overset{\circ}{B}$ can adopt only the $(N+1)$ rational values $0, 1/N, 2/N, ..., N/N$. Hence, either the probabilities also can only take these $(N+1)$ values, or the probabilities can, in general, be represented only approximately by the frequencies. So far, only the second possibility seems to have been pursued.

This representation cannot, of course, make any contribution to the *concrete* contents of the concept of probability. For example, it cannot give any hint what numerical value is to be assumed for the probability of a subset $\overset{\circ}{B}$ of Γ. Nevertheless, Gibbs's representation can be used as a guide to the *formal*

77

properties which every concrete concept of probability should exhibit. Such formal properties are described by the following postulates.

14.1. POSTULATES:

(i) The probability that the initial point $\mathring{x}$ of a mechanical system belongs, at time $\mathring{t}$, to any Lebesgue subset $\mathring{L}$ of the phase space Γ is a non-negative additive set function $\mathring{P}(\mathring{L})$. (For short, it may be called the probability of the set $\mathring{L}$.)

(ii) The probability of the whole phase space at time $\mathring{t}$, $\mathring{P}(\Gamma)$, is equal to 1.

(iii) If $L = \chi(\mathring{L}, \mathring{t}, t)$ is the phase image of any Lebesgue subset $\mathring{L}$ of Γ at time t, then the probability that the moving phase point $x = \chi(\mathring{x}, \mathring{t}, t)$ belongs at time t to the set $L, P(L, t)$, is equal to the probability that the initial point $\mathring{x}$ belongs, at time $\mathring{t}$, to the set $\mathring{L}$ (cf. § 11.2).

(iv) The set function $\mathring{P}(\mathring{L})$ is absolutely continuous (cf. § 8.12).

Examples. If χ denotes a stationary measure-conserving phase flow and J a Lebesgue subset of the phase space Γ of positive finite measure μJ which is invariant with respect to χ, then the set function $\mu(LJ)/\mu J$ (defined for all Lebesgue subsets of Γ) satisfies all the postulates (cf. § 13.6). More generally, if $w(x)$ is a non-negative function which is integrable over Γ and for which $\int_\Gamma w(x)\, dx > 0$, then the set function

$$\frac{\int_L w(x)\, dx}{\int_\Gamma w(x)\, dx}$$

satisfies the postulates. By putting $w(x) = \delta_J(x)$, again the set function $\mu(LJ)/\mu J$ is obtained.

Arguments for the postulates. The first three postulates are immediate consequences of Gibbs's interpretation of the concept of probability. (In fact, they should hold not only for Lebesgue sets, but for all subsets of Γ.)

The fourth postulate of absolute continuity seems at first to contradict Gibbs's representation. For, if $a_1, a_2, \ldots, a_N$ are the initial points of all the systems which form Gibbs's fictitious ensemble, and if $U_\epsilon(a_i)$ is the ϵ-neighbourhood of a_i, then the measure of $\sum_{i=1}^{N} U_\epsilon(a_i)$ is arbitrarily small for sufficiently small ϵ, whereas, on the other hand, the frequency of all the systems the initial points of which lie in $\sum_{i=1}^{N} U_\epsilon(a_i)$ is equal to 1 for all values of ϵ. The postulate of absolute continuity, however, does not contradict the three other postulates, as is shown by the previous examples.

In order to vindicate the last postulate within Gibbs's interpretation as well, it appears to be sufficient to remember that, in general, probabilities are represented by frequencies only approximately. If, therefore, $a_1, \ldots, a_N$ are the initial points of a suitable fictitious ensemble, then the initial points $b_1, \ldots, b_N$ are initial points of such an ensemble, too, if all the distances $|b_i - a_i|$, $i = 1, 2, \ldots, N$, are sufficiently small, say, if $|b_i - a_i| \leqslant \beta$. But then we are no longer entitled to choose the quantity ϵ smaller than β in the consideration of the set $\sum_{i=1}^{N} U_\epsilon(a_i)$. Thus the discrepancy between the fourth postulate and Gibbs's representation is no longer real.

The proper reason for assuming that postulate is its mathematical convenience. For, by Theorem 8.13, the set function $\overset{\circ}{P}(\overset{\circ}{L})$ is now absolutely additive so that Lebesgue's Theorem 8.14 may be applied to it. Thus the rather unmanageable set function can be replaced by a much more convenient point function, and the following theorem is obtained.

14.2. THEOREM. *For every probability distribution* $\overset{\circ}{P}(\overset{\circ}{L})$ *which satisfies the postulates 14.1 there is a "probability density", i.e. a non-negative point function* $\overset{\circ}{w}(\overset{\circ}{x})$ *which is uniquely defined for almost all points* $\overset{\circ}{x}$ *of* Γ, *which is integrable over* Γ, *and for which*

$$\overset{\circ}{P}(\overset{\circ}{L}) = \int_{\overset{\circ}{L}} \overset{\circ}{w}(\overset{\circ}{x})\, d\overset{\circ}{x}$$

for any Lebesgue subset $\overset{\circ}{L}$ *of* Γ. *In particular,*

$$\int_\Gamma \overset{\circ}{w}(\overset{\circ}{x})\, d\overset{\circ}{x} = 1.$$

COROLLARY. The probability distribution

$$P(\mathring{L}, t) \equiv \mathring{P}\{\chi(\mathring{L}, t, \mathring{t})\}$$

(where $\mathring{L}$ denotes any Lebesgue subset of Γ) for the position of the moving phase-point $x = \chi(\mathring{x}, \mathring{t}, t)$ at time t possesses a probability density $w(x, t)$ which is uniquely defined almost everywhere in and integrable over Γ.

Notes. Postulate (iii) is evidently not needed for the derivation of the theorem. Postulate (iv) could have been replaced by the postulate that $\mathring{P}(\mathring{L})$ should not only be additive, but absolutely additive. It might even be that this postulate appears more evident than Postulate (iv). Again, this new postulate would not be a consequence of Gibbs's representative ensemble, but, rather, an additional assumption made for the sake of its mathematical usefulness.

§ 15. On the application of the concept of probability

15.1. The probability distribution $\mathring{P}(\mathring{L})$ or its density $\mathring{w}(\mathring{x})$ is devised to describe quantitatively our knowledge or reasonable suppositions about the position of the initial phase-point $\mathring{x}$ of a given mechanical system. Concerning it, we assume the following rule.

Rule. Let $\mathring{L}$ and $\mathring{L}'$ be any Lebesgue subsets of the phase space Γ. Suppose that, for any reasons, we think it more "probable" (in the sense of the ordinary language of daily life) that the initial point $\mathring{x}$ belongs to $\mathring{L}$ than to $\mathring{L}'$. Then—and only then—we have to put $\mathring{P}(\mathring{L}) > \mathring{P}(\mathring{L}')$. If we are certain that $\mathring{x}$ belongs to $\mathring{L}$, we set $\mathring{P}(\mathring{L}) = 1$. If, conversely, by any computations the result $\mathring{P}(\mathring{L}) = 1 - \eta$ should be obtained where η denotes a non-negative number which is very much smaller than 1, then we shall expect "with practical certainty" that the initial point $\mathring{x}$ of the given system lies in the set $\mathring{L}$.

Notes. "With practical certainty" means that exceptions are possible which, however, are thought so "improbable" that they may be ignored. The more philosophical question, of the proper meaning of the word "probable" in the ordinary language of daily life, is not considered here. For this, the reader may be referred to the literature. The author wishes here only to emphasize that, although it is possible to devise abstract theories of "probability" (along the lines of § 14.1) without any reference to the pre-scientific concept of probability, in his opinion it is not possible to apply them to any problem posed to us by the real world in which we live, without using that pre-scientific concept.

Whether or not a positive number is to be regarded as very small in comparison with unity, depends partly on the objective circumstances, partly on subjective valuation. There is probably nobody who considers the fractions $\frac{1}{2}$ or $\frac{1}{3}$ as very small; as for the fractions $\frac{1}{20}$ or $\frac{1}{30}$, some doubt may exist— but surely not with respect to $\frac{1}{200}$ or $\frac{1}{300}$. In order to fix our ideas, the statement $\eta \ll 1$ will usually be understood as $\eta \leqslant \frac{1}{100}$.

15.2. Immediately, there arise two fundamental problems:

(i) How can the different degrees of subjective certainty be described numerically?

(ii) How can the expectation that the logical consequences drawn from subjectively assumed probabilities are objectively true be justified?

The following example is typical of the second problem. Assume that at first the initial point $\overset{\circ}{x}$ of a given mechanical system is only known to belong to a certain subset $\overset{\circ}{L}$ of Γ. Hence, according to § 15.1, necessarily $\overset{\circ}{P}(\overset{\circ}{L}) = 1$. Now suppose further that in course of time the amount of available information about the system is increased so that, then, it becomes known that $\overset{\circ}{x}$ is a point of the proper subset $\overset{\circ}{L}'$ of $\overset{\circ}{L}$. Therefore now, $\overset{\circ}{P}(\overset{\circ}{L}') = 1$ and $\overset{\circ}{P}(\overset{\circ}{L} - \overset{\circ}{L}') = 0$, whilst before $\overset{\circ}{P}(\overset{\circ}{L} - \overset{\circ}{L}')$ may have been different from zero. Both probability distributions have been assumed according to our best knowledge. But since both are different, at least a part of the conclusions drawn from them will be different. Which of them is "true"?

15.3. As to the first question, it seems possible to adopt a probability distribution without arbitrariness in the following case. Suppose that the initial point $\overset{\circ}{x}$ of a given mechanical system is known to belong to a certain Lebesgue subset A of Γ of finite positive measure (in practice A will always be even bounded), and that this is the only information available about the position of $\overset{\circ}{x}$. Then it "appears reasonable", "is plausible", etc., to put the probability of any measurable subset of A proportional to its measure. Hence

$$\overset{\circ}{P}(\overset{\circ}{L}) = \frac{\mu(A\overset{\circ}{L})}{\mu A}$$

for any Lebesgue subset $\overset{\circ}{L}$ of Γ (cf. § 15.1), and

$$\overset{\circ}{w}(\overset{\circ}{x}) = \frac{\delta_A(\overset{\circ}{x})}{\mu A}$$

for all points $\overset{\circ}{x}$ of Γ (cf. § 14.2).

The methodical principle by which (consciously or unconsciously) the "equipartition of probability" is assumed is always that of sufficient (or here, more properly, of lacking) reason: no sufficient reason can be observed to distinguish any part of the set A from any other part of equal volume with respect to the probability; hence, for parts of equal size, equal probabilities are to be assumed.

This principle has been called "methodical" since it is a "general-subjective" maxim which is inherent to human intellect and guides our mental procedure in such cases as discussed, rather than a proposition about objective reality.

If the set A lies on a surface of the phase space which is determined by one or more known First Integrals of the equations of motion (cf. § 13.6), then it can be dealt with in a similar fashion. The following method, however, seems simpler. The set A (of vanishing measure) is embedded in a suitable bounded set B of very small, but positive, measure, and equipartition of probability is then assumed in B—although this is in contradiction to our knowledge! The error of the observable consequences, can, however, in general, be made as small as we please. Choose, for example, for B the "parallel set" A_ϵ of A. (It is defined as the set of all the points of Γ the distances of which from any point of A are smaller than ϵ.) For sufficiently small values of ϵ, it may be expected that the observable quantities derived from equipartition of probability in A_ϵ differ only little from the corresponding quantities derived from equipartition in A.

In applications, the case of equipartition is by far the most important. Another form of introducing a probability distribution is conceivable in the following case. Assume that a series of measurements of the coordinates of the initial point $\overset{0}{x}$ has been made and that in their result a, each coordinate has the mean square error σ. Then the probability density

$$\overset{0}{w}(\overset{0}{x}) = \left(\frac{1}{\sigma\sqrt{(2\pi)}}\right)^n \exp\left[-(\overset{0}{x}-a)(\overset{0}{x}-a)/2\sigma^2\right]$$

appears as a "reasonable" assumption.

Note. In the literature, Liouville's Theorem 11.4 is sometimes regarded as the proper reason for the assumption of equipartition, and even for the necessity of this assumption. This opinion appears untenable. The probability distribution for the position of the initial point has nothing to do with a more or less accidental property of the phase flow (i.e. with the law according to which the probability develops in course of time). Thus Theorem 16.1 will give the probability distribution as a function of time for general (not necessarily measure-conserving) phase flows, for which Liouville's Theorem does not hold, and in all the subsequent theorems the assumption that there is equipartition of probability is made only exceptionally.

15.4. Although in the above examples the initial probability density $\overset{0}{w}(\overset{0}{x})$ was assumed subjectively, it was, nevertheless, assumed general-subjectively: everybody having the same information would (at least very likely) make the same assumption. Now an example (of a somewhat unconventional kind) will be given in which the individual arbitrariness is considerably greater.

Consider a globular star cluster. Let, at time $\overset{0}{t}$, the number-density $D(r)$ of the bright stars (the only ones which are visible at all) be known by observation as a function of the distance r from the centre of the cluster in the interval $r_1 \leqslant r \leqslant r_2$. The lower limit is positive since, in the core of the cluster, the density of the stars is so large that their images on the photographic plate overlap each other. So it is not possible to count the stars there. Further, assume that the mean square σ^2 of the velocity components of all the visible single stars in the direction to the centre of the cluster from the Sun is empirically known. (The centre of the cluster is here supposed to be at rest.) Then, if $\overset{0}{q}{}^\nu$ is the positional vector and $\overset{0}{p}{}^\nu$ the vector of momentum of the νth star, the following hypothetical assumption seems plausible:

$$\mathring{w}(\mathring{x}) = \prod_{\nu=1}^{n} \{D(|\mathring{q}^{\nu}|) \times \text{function of } \mathring{p}^{\nu} \text{ alone}\}.$$

The function $D(r)$ is here to be extrapolated in any plausible manner. In particular, the hypothetical expression for $\mathring{w}(\mathring{x})$ contains the assumption that the large number of faint stars which are not observable are also similarly distributed in the cluster. For the function of $\mathring{p}^{\nu}$, the expression

$$\text{const.} \exp\left\{-\left(\frac{|\mathring{p}^{\nu}|}{m}\right)^2 \Big/ 2\sigma^2\right\}$$

(where m denotes an average value of the masses of the stars) may be attempted as an hypothesis, by analogy to Schwarzschild's Law which governs the velocity distribution of the stars in the neighbourhood of the Sun. Because of lack of information, however, it has been assumed above that the velocity distribution in the globular cluster is spherically symmetrical, whilst in our Galaxy it is ellipsoidal. Thus, finally,

$$\mathring{w}(\mathring{x}) = \text{const.} \prod_{\nu=1}^{n} \left\{D(|\mathring{q}^{\nu}|) \exp\left[-\left(\frac{|\mathring{p}^{\nu}|}{m}\right)^2 \Big/ 2\sigma^2\right]\right\},$$

where the factor of proportionality is determined by the condition of normalization, which prescribes that

$$\int_{\Gamma} \mathring{w}(\mathring{x})\, d\mathring{x} = 1.$$

Now suppose that later observations show that the mean square velocity σ is a certain non-constant function $\sigma(r)$ of the radius vector r (which is, in fact, very probably true). Then it is again "plausible", "reasonable", etc., to assume that the probability density for the position of any star within the cluster is proportional to $D(r)$. Therefore, it is to be postulated that

$$\int_{\Gamma/\Gamma^{\nu}} \int_{\Gamma_p^{\nu}} \mathring{w}(\mathring{x})\, d(\mathring{x}/\mathring{x}^{\nu})\, dp^{\nu} = \text{const.}\, D(|\mathring{q}^{\nu}|).$$

(For the meaning of the symbol Γ/Γ^{ν}, see § 4.1.) Under the new assumptions, this equation is satisfied if

$$\mathring{w}(\mathring{x}) = \text{const.} \prod_{\nu=1}^{n} \left\{\frac{D(|\mathring{q}^{\nu}|)}{[\sigma(|\mathring{q}^{\nu}|)]^{\frac{3}{2}}} \exp\left[-\left(\frac{|\mathring{p}^{\nu}|}{m}\right)^2 \Big/ 2\sigma^2\right]\right\}.$$

Further information would perhaps suggest, for example, the introduction of different classes of masses of the stars, a dependence of the velocity dispersion on the direction, etc. All additional information would require an appropriate change of the initial probability density.

Note. The initial probability densities just given are open to at least one severe criticism although, at first sight, they do not seem unreasonable. For $\overset{\circ}{w}(\overset{\circ}{x})$ a function has been assumed which is the product of factors depending only on $\overset{\circ}{q}{}^1, \overset{\circ}{q}{}^2, ..., \overset{\circ}{q}{}^n, \overset{\circ}{p}{}^1, \overset{\circ}{p}{}^2, ...$ or $\overset{\circ}{p}{}^n$, in turn. But such a "separation of the variables" certainly does not hold, in general, for the probability density

$$w(x, t) \equiv \overset{\circ}{w}\{\chi(x, t, \overset{\circ}{t})\}$$

at time t. Hence, by the assumption of $\overset{\circ}{w}(\overset{\circ}{x})$, the instant $\overset{\circ}{t}$ has been distinguished in a way which does not necessarily have any objective foundation.

This objection appears irrefutable. On the other hand, it is hard to see how that separation (or some other way of distinguishing the instant $\overset{\circ}{t}$) could be avoided. Hence it seems best to accept $\overset{\circ}{w}(\overset{\circ}{x})$ as a working hypothesis, but as nothing more.

15.5. Thus we have been led to the second fundamental problem of § 15.2. Can it justifiably be expected that the logical consequences drawn from a subjectively assumed probability distribution are objectively true? In the answer, two distinctions are to be made, one with respect to the initial probability distributions, the other one with respect to the conclusions drawn from them.

Initial probability distributions express either:

(a) exclusively certain knowledge, or
(b) include supplementary hypothetical assumptions.

Conclusions drawn from given initial probability distributions may be

(α) topological,
(β) measure-theoretical, or
(γ) statistical,

in their mathematical character.

Examples of (a) and (b) have been given in § 15.3 and § 15.4. The alternative (α) means that if the initial point $\overset{\circ}{x}$ of a given

mechanical system is known to belong to a certain Lebesgue
subset $\overset{o}{L}$ of the phase space Γ of finite positive measure, and
if, according to the Rule 15.1, the initial probability density
$\overset{o}{w}(\overset{o}{x})$ is defined by

$$\overset{o}{w}(\overset{o}{x}) = \frac{\delta_{\overset{o}{L}}(\overset{o}{x})}{\mu \overset{o}{L}},$$

then all those of its consequences which are equivalent to the
statement that $\chi(\overset{o}{x}, \overset{o}{l}, t) \in \chi(\overset{o}{L}, \overset{o}{l}, t)$ are certain knowledge. Propositions based only on topological and measure-theoretical
considerations (like Poincaré's Recurrence Theorem 12.1) which
refer to almost all points of such a set $\overset{o}{L}$ yield a practically
certain knowledge (β). Mean values, dispersions, etc., however,
which are necessarily based on some assumption about the
probability distribution, cannot be regarded as guaranteed
knowledge (γ). The predictions of every probability theory can
be wrong since it is just the very essence of such a theory to
substitute "plausible assumptions" for lacking data (although
sometimes the assumptions may appear so very plausible—
either by the natural inclination of human intellect or habits
of thought—that they are not felt as assumptions at all). Thus,
for instance, the statistical predictions for a game of dice
will be wrong if, according to Rule 15.1, they are based
on the probability $\frac{1}{6}$ for each face, when, in fact, the dice is
"false".

In such cases, probability theory is, in the author's view, to
be regarded only as a method to devise reasonable hypotheses
which have to be checked indirectly by comparison of its
consequences with the corresponding observations. In fact,
this holds more or less for the application of every theory to
reality. Application is always also a matter of scientific judge-
ment and not of theory alone. For a deeper discussion of these
questions the reader may be referred to the literature.

In summary, it may be stated that only in the case $(a\alpha)$
must the application of the theory to reality be true. In the
case $(a\beta)$, there is practically no doubt that the propositions
of the theory will always be verified by the observations. In
all the other cases, the theory can yield only reasonable hypotheses devised methodically. A principal reason why, in many
cases, these hypotheses do work, will be given in § 21.4.

In the following chapters, the problem of the initial probability distribution will no longer be touched. Instead, the mathematical conclusions that can be drawn from a given initial distribution will be investigated.

References

For the axiomatics of the theory of probability, see, for instance, Cramèr's book [10]. One of the first axiomatics of probability theory was given by Kolmogoroff [26]. It had a considerable influence on the development of ideas.

[26] KOLMOGOROFF, A. N., Grundzüge der Wahrscheinlichkeitsrechung (Ergebnisse der Mathematik, Springer, 1932).

The philosophical problems which are connected with the concept of probability and its application have been discussed by the author in the following paper:

[27] KURTH, R., Über den Begriff der Wahrscheinlichkeit. Philosophia Naturalis, 5, 413–429, 1958.

Rather different views have been taken, for example, by Reichenbach and v. Mises:

[28] REICHENBACH, H., Wahrscheinlichkeitslehre.

[29] v. MISES, R., Wahrscheinlichkeit, Statistik und Wahrheit, Wien, 1951.

Gibbs, in his classical treatise [30], hardly touched the problems of probability connected with the foundations of statistical mechanics, and the same is true for nearly all presentations of the subject known to me. Reference to Liouville's Theorem was made, for example, by Fowler [31]. On the whole, Gibbs's book is still distinguished by the clarity of its argument and presentation.

[30] GIBBS, J. W., Elementary Principles in Statistical Mechanics, New York and London, 1902.

[31] FOWLER, R. H., Statistische Mechanik, Leipzig, 1931.

The facts and data which are significant for an eventual application of statistical mechanics to stellar systems are given in a coherent presentation by

[32] BECKER, W., Sterne und Sternsysteme, Dresden and Leipzig, 1950.

or, in form of tables, by

[33] LANDOLT-BÖRNSTEIN, Zahlenwarte und Funktionen aus Astronomie und Geophysik, Berlin, Göttingen, Heidelberg, 1952.

or, again, by

[34] ALLEN, C. W., Astrophysical Quantities, London, 1955.

CHAPTER V

PROBABILITY DISTRIBUTIONS WHICH DEPEND ON TIME

§ 16. Mechanical systems with general equations of motion

16.1. THEOREM. *The probability density $w(x, t)$ for the position of the moving phase point at time t (cf. Corollary 14.2) is given by*

$$w(x, t) = \frac{\mathring{w}\{\chi(x, t, \mathring{t})\}}{\Delta\{\chi(x, t, \mathring{t}) \mathring{t}, t\}}.$$

Here, $\mathring{w}(\mathring{x})$ denotes the density of the initial probability distribution and $\Delta(\mathring{x}, \mathring{t}, t)$ denotes the Jacobian determinant $|(\partial/\partial \mathring{x}_j) \chi_i(\mathring{x}, \mathring{t}, t)|$ of the phase mapping $x = \chi(\mathring{x}, \mathring{t}, t)$.

Proof. Let $\mathring{L}$ and L be any Lebesgue subsets of the phase space Γ, $\mathring{P}(\mathring{L})$ be the initial probability distribution at time $\mathring{t}$, and $P(L, t)$ that at time t. Then, by § 14.1 (iii),

$$P(L, t) = \mathring{P}(\mathring{L})$$

if

$$L = \chi(\mathring{L}, \mathring{t}, t),$$

or,

$$\int_L w(x, t)\, dx = \int_{\mathring{L}} \mathring{w}(\mathring{x})\, d\mathring{x},$$

by § 14.2. Now introduce $\mathring{x}$ as an integration variable on the left-hand side, instead of x. Thus

$$\int_{\mathring{L}} w\{\chi(\mathring{x}, \mathring{t}, t), t\}\, \Delta(\mathring{x}, \mathring{t}, t)\, d\mathring{x} = \int_{\mathring{L}} \mathring{w}(\mathring{x})\, d\mathring{x},$$

by Theorem 11.5. Hence, by Theorem 8.14,

$$w\{\chi(\mathring{x}, \mathring{t}, t), t\}\, \Delta(\mathring{x}, \mathring{t}, t) = \mathring{w}(\mathring{x})$$

for almost all points $\mathring{x}$ and fixed instants $\mathring{t}$ and t. At those points $\mathring{x}$ for which the equation does not hold, define $w\{\chi(\mathring{x}, \mathring{t}, t), t\}$ anew in such a manner that the equation holds. Now replace $\chi(\mathring{x}, \mathring{t}, t)$ by x and $\mathring{x}$ by $\chi(x, t, \mathring{t})$, and divide by $\Delta\{\chi(x, t, \mathring{t}), \mathring{t}, t\}$, which is possible since (by Theorem 11.1) $\Delta > 0$. The result is the equation given in the theorem.

16.2. THEOREM. *Let the initial probability density $\mathring{w}(\mathring{x})$ possess derivatives with respect to $\mathring{x}_1, ..., \mathring{x}_n$ which are continuous functions of $\mathring{x}$. Further, assume that the right-hand sides $X_i(x, t)$, $i = 1, 2, ..., n$, of the equations of motion $\dot{x} = X(x, t)$ possess second-order derivatives with respect to $x_1, ..., x_n$ which are continuous functions of (x, t). Then the probability density $w(x, t)$ of the moving phase point x at time t possesses derivatives with respect to $x_1, ..., x_n, t$ which are continuous functions of (x, t), and $w(x, t)$ satisfies the differential equation*

$$\frac{\partial w}{\partial t} + \sum_{i=1}^{n} \frac{\partial}{\partial x_i} (wX_i) = 0.$$

Proof. The existence and continuity of the derivatives of $w(x, t)$ follow from the Theorems 16.1 and 6.6. For the proof of the differential equation, differentiate the equation

$$w\{\chi(\mathring{x}, \mathring{t}, t), t\} \Delta(\mathring{x}, \mathring{t}, t) = \mathring{w}(\mathring{x})$$

(see Proof 16.1) with respect to t, to give

$$\left\{ \frac{\partial w(\chi, t)}{\partial t} + \sum_{j=1}^{n} \frac{\partial w(\chi, t)}{\partial \chi_j} \frac{\partial \chi_j(\mathring{x}, \mathring{t}, t)}{\partial t} \right\} \Delta(\mathring{x}, \mathring{t}, t) +$$

$$+ w(\chi, t) \frac{\partial \Delta(\mathring{x}, \mathring{t}, t)}{\partial t} = 0,$$

replace $\dfrac{\partial \Delta}{\partial t}$ by $\Delta \sum\limits_{k=1}^{n} X_{kk}(\chi, t)$

(according to Theorem 11.3), to give

$$\left\{ \frac{\partial w(\chi, t)}{\partial t} + \sum_{j=1}^{n} \frac{\partial w(\chi, t)}{\partial \chi_j} \frac{\partial \chi_j(\mathring{x}, \mathring{t}, t)}{\partial t} + \sum_{j=1}^{n} X_{jj}(\chi, t) w(\chi, t) \right\} \Delta(\mathring{x}, \mathring{t}, t) = 0,$$

divide by $\Delta(\mathring{x}, \mathring{t}, t)$, which is positive (by Theorem 11.3), substitute $X_j\{\chi(\mathring{x}, \mathring{t}, t), t\}$ for $\partial \chi_j(\mathring{x}, \mathring{t}, t)/\partial t$ (on account of the equations of motion), and finally, replace the independent variables $(\mathring{x}, t)$ by the independent variables (x, t) by means of the relation $x = \chi(\mathring{x}, \mathring{t}, t)$. The result is the differential equation of the theorem.

16.3. Let Γ' be a k-dimensional sub-space of the phase space Γ, L' be a subset of Γ' which possesses a k-dimensional Lebesgue measure, and x' the k-dimensional component of the vector x which belongs to Γ'. Then the probability $P'(L', t)$ that, at time t, the point x' lies in L' equals the probability that, at the same time, x belongs to the cylindric set $L' \times (\Gamma/\Gamma')$. Thus

$$P'(L', t) \equiv P\{L' \times (\Gamma/\Gamma'), t\}.$$

By § 14.3, the probability distribution $P'(L', t)$ can be described by means of a probability density $w'(x', t)$, which is defined for almost all points x' of Γ' (the instant t being kept fixed). For these points,

$$w'(x', t) = \int_{\Gamma/\Gamma'} w(x, t)\, \mathrm{d}(x/x').$$

(Cf. Fubini's Theorem 8.15.) For the rest of Γ', define $w'(x', t)$ by this equation.

DEFINITIONS. The function

$$w_{(x')}(x, t) = \begin{cases} \dfrac{w(x, t)}{w'(x', t)} & \text{if } w' > 0, \\[2mm] 0 & \text{if } w' = 0 \end{cases}$$

is called the density of the *probability in* Γ/Γ' *conditional with respect to* x'. It describes a probability distribution of x/x' for a given value of x'. Now let $f(x, t)$ be any function defined in $\Gamma \times T$ (where T denotes the axis of time) for which the integral

$$\bar{f}^{(x')}(x', t) \equiv \int_{\Gamma/\Gamma'} f(x, t)\, w_{(x')}(x, t)\, \mathrm{d}(x/x')$$

exists at every moment t. Then the quantity $\bar{f}^{(x')}$ is said to be the *conditional expectation value* of the function $f(x, t)$ with respect to x' at time t.

16.4. THEOREM. *Let the initial probability density* $\overset{\circ}{w}(\overset{\circ}{x})$ *be different from zero only in a bounded subset of the phase space* Γ, *and possess derivatives with respect to* $\overset{\circ}{x}_1, \ldots, \overset{\circ}{x}_n$ *which are continuous functions of* $\overset{\circ}{x}$. *Suppose, further, that the right-hand sides* $X_i(x, t)$ *of the equations of motion* $\dot{x} = X(x, t)$ *possess second-order derivatives with respect to* $x_1, \ldots, x_n$ *which depend continuously on* (x, t). *Then the probability density* $w'(x', t)$ *in the sub-space* Γ' *(extended by the coordinates* $x_{n_1}, x_{n_2}, \ldots, x_{n_k}$*) possesses derivatives with respect to* $x_{n_1}, \ldots, x_{n_k}, t$ *which are continuous functions of* (x', t), *and satisfies the differential equation*

$$\frac{\partial w'}{\partial t} + \sum_{j=1}^{n} \frac{\partial}{\partial x_{n_j}} \left(w' \overline{X_{n_j}}^{(x')} \right) = 0.$$

Notes. A comparison of this theorem with Theorem 16.2 shows that the probability distribution in Γ' develops in such a fashion as if in Γ' a phase flow were generated by the equations of motion

$$\dot{x}_{nj} = \bar{X}_{nj}^{(x')} (x',t), \quad j = 1,\ldots,k.$$

If, for example, in a system of mass-points, Γ' is the phase space of a single mass-point, then the probability of this particle in its phase space Γ' develops in such a manner as if the particle were subjected to the conditional expectation value of the whole force acting on it, the restricting condition being the position of the particle in Γ'.

The assumption that $\overset{o}{w}(\overset{o}{x})$ differs from zero only in a bounded subset of Γ is not necessary, but has been introduced only for mathematical convenience. For, by Theorem 5.5, the probability density $w(x,t)$ is also, at any time t, different from zero only in a bounded subset of Γ. This facilitates the necessary integrations a little. This assumption does not, of course, imply any essential physical restriction.

Proof. Integrate the differential equation of Theorem 16.2 over Γ/Γ':

$$\int_{\Gamma/\Gamma'} \frac{\partial w}{\partial t} \,\mathrm{d}(x/x') + \sum_{i=1}^{n} \int_{\Gamma/\Gamma'} \frac{\partial}{\partial x_i} (wX_i) \,\mathrm{d}(x/x') = 0.$$

The first term equals $\partial w'/\partial t$. If x_i is a coordinate of x/x', the corresponding term of the sum vanishes. If x_i is a coordinate of x', then

$$\int_{\Gamma/\Gamma'} \frac{\partial}{\partial x_i} (wX_i) \,\mathrm{d}(x/x') = \frac{\partial}{\partial x_i} \int_{\Gamma/\Gamma'} wX_i \,\mathrm{d}(x/x')$$

$$= \frac{\partial}{\partial x_i} \int_{\Gamma/\Gamma'} w'w_{(x')} X_i \,\mathrm{d}(x/x')$$

$$= \frac{\partial}{\partial x_i} (w' \bar{X}_i^{(x')}).$$

This proves the theorem.

16.5. THEOREM. *Let $v(x,t)$ be a function which, for all values of (x,t), possesses continuous derivatives with respect to*

$x_1, x_2, \ldots, x_n, t$ *and satisfies the two conditions*

$$\frac{\partial v}{\partial t} + \sum_{\nu=1}^{n} \frac{\partial}{\partial x_\nu} (v X_\nu) = 0 \quad \text{for all } (x, t),$$

and $\qquad\qquad v(x, t) = \overset{0}{w}(x) \quad \text{for all } x.$

Here $\overset{0}{w}(x)$ denotes a function which possesses continuous derivatives with respect to $x_1, \ldots, x_n$ everywhere in Γ, and the X_ν's are continuous functions of (x, t) which have continuous second-order derivatives with respect to $x_1, \ldots, x_n$ for all values of (x, t). Let $\chi(\overset{0}{x}, \overset{0}{t}, t)$ be the general solution of the system of ordinary differential equations, $\dot{x} = X(x, t)$, such that $\overset{0}{x} = \chi(\overset{0}{x}, \overset{0}{t}, \overset{0}{t})$, and $\Delta(\overset{0}{x}, \overset{0}{t}, t)$ denote the Jacobian determinant

$$\left| \frac{\partial}{\partial x_j} \chi_i(\overset{0}{x}, \overset{0}{t}, t) \right|.$$

Then $\qquad\qquad v(x, t) \equiv \dfrac{\overset{0}{w}\{\chi(x, t, \overset{0}{t})\}}{\Delta\{\chi(x, t, \overset{0}{t}), \overset{0}{t}, t\}}.$

The theorem is proved by the inversion of the proof 16.2.

Note. By the theorem, the probability density $w(x, t)$ is uniquely determined by the initial density $\overset{0}{w}(x)$ and the differential equation of Theorem 16.2 (or 16.5). Now, if the conditional expectation values $\bar{X}_i^{(x')}(x', t)$ were known, then, by the Theorems 16.4 and 16.5, it would be possible to compute the probability density $w'(x', t)$ in Γ' for any given initial density $\overset{0}{w}'(\overset{0}{x})$ without calculating the density $w(x, t)$ in Γ. This would be an enormous advantage: the number n of the equations of motion is very large in all applications so that even an approximate numerical computation of the n functions $\chi_i(\overset{0}{x}, \overset{0}{t}, t)$, $i = 1, 2, \ldots, n$, or of the probability density $w(x, t)$ is, in general, completely impracticable (cf. § 1). But observations refer only to sub-spaces Γ' of Γ whose number of dimensions, k, are small; strictly speaking, observations are made only in the 3-dimensional real space. Thus the Theorems 16.4 and 16.5 appear to offer the possibility of calculating all the observationally relevant quantities directly, without the vast and impassable detour through the n-dimensional phase space.

There is, however, still a major difficulty. Actually, the functions $\bar{X}_i^{(x')}(x', t)$ are not known since their computation already supposes the explicit knowledge of $w(x, t)$. In order to reconnoitre a path through this difficulty, we shall, in the following section, consider particular cases; namely, systems with Hamiltonian or even Newtonian equations of motion.

§ 17. Hamiltonian and Newtonian systems

17.1. THEOREM. *For mechanical systems with Hamiltonian equations of motion, the probability density $w(x, t)$ for the position of the moving phase point x in the phase space Γ at time t, is invariant with respect to the phase flow χ, and*

$$w(x, t) \equiv \overset{\circ}{w}\{\chi(x, t, \overset{\circ}{t})\},$$

where $\overset{\circ}{w}(x)$ denotes the probability density at time $\overset{\circ}{t}$.

Proof. By Liouville's Theorem 11.4, $\Delta(\overset{\circ}{x}, \overset{\circ}{t}, t) \equiv 1$, where $\Delta(\overset{\circ}{x}, \overset{\circ}{t}, t)$ denotes the Jacobian determinant $|\partial \chi_i / \partial \overset{\circ}{x}_j|$. Hence, by Theorem 16.1,

$$w(x, t) \equiv \overset{\circ}{w}\{\chi(x, t, \overset{\circ}{t})\},$$

or $\qquad w\{\chi(\overset{\circ}{x}, \overset{\circ}{t}, t), t\} \equiv \overset{\circ}{w}(\overset{\circ}{x}) \equiv w(\overset{\circ}{x}, \overset{\circ}{t})$:

i.e. $w(x, t)$ is invariant.

Note. The theorem appears to be intuitively obvious. The flow χ conserves the "probability element" $dP = w \, dx$ because of Postulate (iii) of § 16.1. Similarly, it conserves the "volume element" dx, according to Liouville's Theorem, and also, therefore, the quotient of both these quantities, the probability density w.

17.2. THEOREM. *For a Hamiltonian system whose equations of motion read $\dot{x} = X(x, t)$ or*

$$\left. \begin{aligned} \dot{p}_\nu &= -H_{q_\nu}(p, q, t), \\ \dot{q}_\nu &= +H_{p_\nu}(p, q, t), \end{aligned} \right\}$$

the probability density $w(x, t)$ satisfies the differential equation

$$\frac{\partial w}{\partial t} + \sum_\nu \frac{\partial w}{\partial x_\nu} X_\nu = 0$$

(which is usually named after Liouville) or

$$\frac{\partial w}{\partial t} + \sum_\nu \left(\frac{\partial w}{\partial q_\nu} \frac{\partial H}{\partial p_\nu} - \frac{\partial w}{\partial p_\nu} \frac{\partial H}{\partial q_\nu} \right) = 0,$$

provided that the initial probability density $\overset{\circ}{w}(x)$ possesses derivatives with respect to $x_1, \ldots, x_n$ which are continuous functions of x.

Proof. By Theorem 16.2,

$$\frac{\partial w}{\partial t} + \sum_\nu \frac{\partial w}{\partial x_\nu} X_\nu + w \sum_\nu \frac{\partial X_\nu}{\partial x_\nu} = 0,$$

and this equation implies the theorem, given the assumptions made in its statement.

Note. Liouville's equation can sometimes be used to decide whether a given (differentiable) function $v(p,q,t)$ is admissible as a probability density of a Hamiltonian system. For $v(p,q,t)$ has to satisfy the following three conditions, which are necessary and, in formal respects, also sufficient,

(i) $v(p,q,t) \geqslant 0,$

(ii) $\int_\Gamma v(p,q,t)\,\mathrm{d}(p,q) = 1,$

(iii) $\frac{\partial v}{\partial t} + \sum_\nu \left(\frac{\partial v}{\partial q_\nu} \frac{\partial H}{\partial p_\nu} - \frac{\partial v}{\partial p_\nu} \frac{\partial H}{\partial q_\nu} \right) \equiv 0,$

for all values of p, q and t (cf. § 14.1). (For non-differentiable functions $v(p,q,t)$, condition (iii) is to be replaced by the more general one that v is a First Integral of the equations of motion. See Theorem 17.1.) It seems that not all the functions which have been used as probability densities in Statistical Mechanics satisfy the above conditions. Hence, the conclusions drawn from them are objectionable on logical grounds; they may be, but they need not be, wrong, since the result of a fallacious inference can be either correct or incorrect.

17.3. THEOREM. *Let the system of ordinary differential equations $\dot{x} = g(x,t)$ where $x = (x_1, ..., x_n)$ have a solution $x = \psi(\mathring{x}, \mathring{t}, t)$ which is defined for all values of $\mathring{x}, \mathring{t}, t$, which has continuous derivatives with respect to all its arguments and satisfies the initial conditions $\mathring{x} = \psi(\mathring{x}, \mathring{t}, \mathring{t})$. Further, let $\mathring{v}(x)$ be a function which is defined for all values of x and possesses continuous derivatives with respect to all its arguments. Then there is exactly one solution $v(x,t)$ of the differential equation*

$$\frac{\partial v}{\partial t} + \sum_{\nu=1}^n \frac{\partial v}{\partial x_\nu} g_\nu(x,t) = 0$$

which satisfies the initial condition

$$v(x, \overset{0}{t}) \equiv \overset{0}{v}(x).$$

It is defined for all values of x and t, is a First Integral of the system of differential equations $\dot{x} = g(x,t)$, and reads

$$v(x, t) \equiv \overset{0}{v}\{\psi(x, t, \overset{0}{t})\}.$$

The proof is analogous to the proofs of the Theorems 16.2 and 16.5.

17.4. THEOREM. *Let*

$$x' = (p', q') = (p_{n_1}, p_{n_2}, ..., p_{n_\kappa}, \quad q_{n_1}, q_{n_2}, ..., q_{n_\kappa})$$

be a component of the phase vector $x = (p, q)$ of a mechanical system having a Hamiltonian function $H(p, q, t)$. Suppose that the initial probability density $\overset{0}{w}(x)$ in the phase space Γ differs from zero only in a bounded subset of Γ, and that it possesses continuous derivatives with respect to all its arguments $p_1, p_2, ..., q_n$ everywhere in Γ. Then the probability density $w'(x', t)$ in the sub-space Γ' of all components x' satisfies the equation

$$\frac{\partial w'}{\partial t} + \sum_{\kappa=1}^{k} \left\{ \frac{\partial}{\partial q_{n_\kappa}} \left(w' \frac{\overline{\partial H^{(x')}}}{\partial p_{n_\kappa}} \right) - \frac{\partial}{\partial p_{n_\kappa}} \left(w' \frac{\overline{\partial H^{(x')}}}{\partial q_{n_\kappa}} \right) \right\} = 0.$$

Here $\overline{\partial H^{(x')}}/\partial p_{n_\kappa}$ and $\overline{\partial H^{(x')}}/\partial q_{n_\kappa}$ denote the conditional expectation values of $\partial H/\partial p_{n_\kappa}$ and $\partial H/\partial q_{n_\kappa}$ with respect to x' (cf. 16.3).

COROLLARY. If there are continuous second-order derivatives of $w(x, t)$ with respect to $p_1, ..., q_n$, then $w'(x', t)$ also satisfies the equation

$$\frac{\partial w'}{\partial t} + \sum_{x=1}^{k} \left(\frac{\partial w'}{\partial q_{n_\kappa}} \frac{\partial \bar{H}^{(x')}}{\partial p_{n_\kappa}} - \frac{\partial w'}{\partial p_{n_\kappa}} \frac{\partial \bar{H}^{(x')}}{\partial q_{n_\kappa}} \right)$$

$$= \sum_{\kappa=1}^{k} \int_{\Gamma/\Gamma'} \left\{ \frac{\partial(w'H)}{\partial q_{n_\kappa}} \frac{\partial w_{(x')}}{\partial p_{n_\kappa}} - \frac{\partial(w'H)}{\partial p_{n_\kappa}} \frac{\partial w_{(x')}}{\partial q_{n_\kappa}} \right\} \mathrm{d}(x/x')$$

where $w_{(x')}(x, t)$ denotes the conditional probability density in Γ/Γ' (cf. 16.3).

Proof. The equation of the theorem is an immediate consequence of Theorem 16.4. For the proof of the corollary, transform the expressions $\overline{\partial H^{(x')}}/\partial p_{n_\kappa}$, $\overline{\partial H^{(x')}}/\partial q_{n_\kappa}$ of the equation of the theorem by means of the following relations:

$$\frac{\partial \bar{H}^{(x')}}{\partial p_{n_\kappa}} = \frac{\partial}{\partial p_{n_\kappa}} \int_{\Gamma/\Gamma'} H w_{(x')} \, \mathrm{d}(x/x')$$

$$= \int_{\Gamma/\Gamma'} \frac{\partial H}{\partial p_{n_\kappa}} w_{(x')} \, \mathrm{d}(x/x') + \int_{\Gamma/\Gamma'} H \frac{\partial w_{(x')}}{\partial p_{n_\kappa}} \, \mathrm{d}(x/x')$$

$$= \frac{\overline{\partial H}^{(x')}}{\partial p_{n_\kappa}} + \int_{\Gamma/\Gamma'} H \frac{\partial w_{(x')}}{\partial p_{n_\kappa}} \, \mathrm{d}(x/x')$$

and a similar relation for $\partial \bar{H}^{(x')}/\partial q_{n_\kappa}$. Apply them to the equation of the theorem and arrange the terms in such a fashion that its left-hand side becomes the same as that of the equation of the corollary. The right-hand side then reads

$$\sum_{\kappa=1}^{k} \left\{ \frac{\partial}{\partial q_{n_\kappa}} \left[w' \int_{\Gamma/\Gamma'} H \frac{\partial w_{(x)}}{\partial p_{n_\kappa}} \, \mathrm{d}(x/x') \right] - \right.$$

$$\left. - \frac{\partial}{\partial p_{n_\kappa}} \left[w' \int_{\Gamma/\Gamma'} H \frac{\partial w_{(x)}}{\partial q_{n_\kappa}} \, \mathrm{d}(x/x') \right] \right\}$$

$$= \sum_{\kappa=1}^{k} \left\{ \frac{\partial}{\partial q_{n_\kappa}} \int_{\Gamma/\Gamma'} (w' H) \frac{\partial w_{(x)}}{\partial p_{n_\kappa}} \, \mathrm{d}(x/x') - \right.$$

$$\left. - \frac{\partial}{\partial p_{n_\kappa}} \int_{\Gamma/\Gamma'} (w' H) \frac{\partial w_{(x)}}{\partial q_{n_\kappa}} \, \mathrm{d}(x/x') \right\}$$

$$= \sum_{\kappa=1}^{k} \int_{\Gamma/\Gamma'} \left\{ \frac{\partial (w' H)}{\partial q_{n_\kappa}} \frac{\partial w_{(x)}}{\partial p_{n_\kappa}} - \frac{\partial (w' H)}{\partial p_{n_\kappa}} \frac{\partial w_{(x)}}{\partial p_{n_\kappa}} \right\} \mathrm{d}(x/x'),$$

and this proves the Corollary.

17.5. THEOREM. *Let*

$$H(x) \equiv \frac{1}{2} \sum_{\nu=1}^{n} \frac{p^\nu p^\nu}{m^\nu} + V(q, t)$$

be the Hamiltonian function of a system of n mass-points where

$$V(q, t) \equiv \sum_{\nu=1}^{n} V^\nu(q^\nu, t) + \frac{1}{2} \sum_{\lambda=1}^{n} \sum_{\nu=1}^{n} V^{\lambda\nu}(q^\lambda, q^\nu, t)$$

is the potential of the system,

$$V^{\lambda\lambda} \equiv 0,$$

m^ν is the mass,

$$p^\nu = (p_1^\nu, p_2^\nu, p_3^\nu)$$

is the momentum,

$$q^\nu = (q_1^\nu, q_2^\nu, q_3^\nu)$$

is the vector of position of the νth particle, and

$$p = (p^1, \ldots, p^n), \quad q = (q^1, \ldots, q^n), \quad x^\nu = (p^\nu, q^\nu).$$

Further, let $w^\nu(x^\nu, t)$ be the probability density of the νth mass-point in its phase space Γ^ν, $w^{\lambda\nu}(x^\lambda, x^\nu, t)$ be the probability density of the pair of particles (λ, ν) in $\Gamma^{\lambda\nu} = \Gamma^\lambda \times \Gamma^\nu$, and

$$\omega^{\lambda\nu}(x^\lambda, x^\nu, t) \equiv w^{\lambda\nu} - w^\lambda w^\nu.$$

Assume that the initial probability density $\overset{0}{w}(x)$ in the phase space Γ possesses continuous second-order derivatives with respect to $p_1^1, \ldots, q_3^n$, that it differs from zero only in a bounded subset of Γ, and that the potential $V(q, t)$ has continuous third-order derivatives with respect to $q_1^1, \ldots, q_3^n$. Then $w^\lambda(x^\lambda, t)$ satisfies the equation

$$\frac{\partial w^\lambda}{\partial t} + \sum_{\kappa=1}^{3} \left(\frac{\partial w^\lambda}{\partial q_\kappa^\lambda} \frac{\partial H^\lambda}{\partial p_\kappa^\lambda} - \frac{\partial w^\lambda}{\partial p_\kappa^\lambda} \frac{\partial H^\lambda}{\partial q_\kappa^\lambda} \right)$$

$$= \sum_{\nu=1}^{n} \sum_{\kappa=1}^{3} \int_{\Gamma^\nu} \left(\frac{\partial V^{\lambda\nu}}{\partial q_\kappa^\nu} \frac{\partial \omega^{\lambda\nu}}{\partial p_\kappa^\nu} - \frac{\partial V^{\lambda\nu}}{\partial p_\kappa^\nu} \frac{\partial \omega^{\lambda\nu}}{\partial q_\kappa^\nu} \right) dx^\nu,$$

where

$$H^\lambda \equiv \frac{p^\lambda p^\lambda}{2m^\lambda} + U^\lambda(q^\lambda, t)$$

and

$$U^\lambda \equiv V^\lambda(q^\lambda, t) + \sum_{\nu=1}^{n} \int_{\Gamma^\nu} V^{\lambda\nu}(q^\lambda, q^\nu, t) w^\nu(x^\nu, t) \, dx^\nu.$$

Note. The last term of the differential equation for w^λ vanishes and has been added only for formal symmetry.

Proof. By Corollary 6.6, the solution functions $\chi_i(\overset{0}{x}, \overset{0}{t}, t)$ of the equations of motion possess continuous second-order derivatives with respect to the components of x. Hence, by Theorem § 17.1, $w(x, t)$ has continuous second-order derivatives with respect to the components of x. Now Corollary 17.4 yields the statement of the theorem after replacing $w^{\lambda\nu}$ by $w^\lambda w^\nu + \omega^{\lambda\nu}$ on the left-hand side of the equation of that corollary.

COROLLARY. If $\omega^{\lambda\nu} \equiv 0$, then w^{λ} is a First Integral of the equations of motion

$$\left. \begin{aligned} \dot{p}_{\kappa}^{\lambda} &= -\frac{\partial H^{\lambda}}{\partial q_{\kappa}^{\lambda}}, \\ \dot{q}_{\kappa}^{\lambda} &= +\frac{\partial H^{\lambda}}{\partial p_{\kappa}^{\lambda}}, \end{aligned} \right\} \quad \kappa = 1, 2, 3,$$

and therefore satisfies the corresponding Liouville equation. (For the proof, see the Theorems 17.2 and 17.3.)

Notes. The equation of the theorem is an exact formulation and generalization of an equation which is known in the literature of physics as "Boltzmann's equation". This equation, however, is not given here since no rigorous derivation seems to be known and, in fact, its consequences appear to contradict Poincaré's Recurrence Theorem 12.2 (cf. §§ 19.5 and 24.4). Hence it is based on assumptions essentially different from those of the present investigation.

In the following, the equation will be applied to a system of which all the particles are "equal". First, the concept of "equality", or "equivalence", will be defined.

17.6. DEFINITION. Two particles 1 and 2 of a system of n mass-points are said to be *equivalent* if

$$w(x^1, x^2, x^3, \ldots, x^n, t) \equiv w(x^2, x^1, x^3, \ldots, x^n, t).$$

Notes. If the mass-points 1 and 2 and, further, the mass-points 2 and 3 are equivalent, then the mass-points 1 and 3 are also equivalent.

Proof.

$$w(x^1, x^2, x^3, \ldots, x^n, t) \equiv w(x^2, x^1, x^3, \ldots, x^n, t)$$
$$\equiv w(x^2, x^3, x^1, \ldots, x^n, t)$$
$$\equiv w(x^3, x^2, x^1, \ldots, x^n, t). \qquad \text{Q.E.D.}$$

Hence the set of all the mass-points can be divided into classes in such a manner that any two mass-points belonging to the same class are equivalent, whereas any two mass-points belonging to different classes are not equivalent.

The symmetry of the Hamiltonian function $H(x, t)$ with respect to x^1 and x^2, say, implies the equality of both the masses m^1

and m^2. But, of course, the equality of masses does not imply the equivalence of the particles.

17.7. THEOREM. *If both the Hamiltonian function $H(x, t)$ and the initial probability density $\overset{o}{w}(x)$ of a system of mass-points are symmetrical with respect to the 6-dimensional position-momentum-vector of any two particles, then these two particles are equivalent.*

Proof. For the right-hand sides of the equations of motion $\dot{x} = X(x, t)$ we obtain

$$
\begin{cases}
X^1(x^1, x^2, x^3, \ldots, x^n, t) \equiv X^2(x^2, x^1, x^3, \ldots, x^n, t), \\
X^2(x^1, x^2, x^3, \ldots, x^n, t) \equiv X^1(x^2, x^1, x^3, \ldots, x^n, t), \\
X^3(x^1, x^2, x^3, \ldots, x^n, t) \equiv X^3(x^2, x^1, x^3, \ldots, x^n, t), \\
\ldots \ldots \ldots \ldots \ldots \ldots \ldots \ldots \ldots \ldots \ldots \ldots \ldots \ldots \\
X^n(x^1, x^2, x^3, \ldots, x^n, t) \equiv X^n(x^2, x^1, x^3, \ldots, x^n, t).
\end{cases}
$$

From these, we shall derive that

$$
\begin{cases}
\chi^1(\overset{o}{x}{}^1, \overset{o}{x}{}^2, \overset{o}{x}{}^3, \ldots, \overset{o}{x}{}^n, \overset{o}{t}, t) \equiv \chi^2(\overset{o}{x}{}^2, \overset{o}{x}{}^1, \overset{o}{x}{}^3, \ldots, \overset{o}{x}{}^n, \overset{o}{t}, t), \\
\chi^2(\overset{o}{x}{}^1, \overset{o}{x}{}^2, \overset{o}{x}{}^3, \ldots, \overset{o}{x}{}^n, \overset{o}{t}, t) \equiv \chi^1(\overset{o}{x}{}^2, \overset{o}{x}{}^1, \overset{o}{x}{}^3, \ldots, \overset{o}{x}{}^n, \overset{o}{t}, t), \\
\chi^3(\overset{o}{x}{}^1, \overset{o}{x}{}^2, \overset{o}{x}{}^3, \ldots, \overset{o}{x}{}^n, \overset{o}{t}, t) \equiv \chi^3(\overset{o}{x}{}^2, \overset{o}{x}{}^1, \overset{o}{x}{}^3, \ldots, \overset{o}{x}{}^n, \overset{o}{t}, t), \\
\ldots \ldots \ldots \ldots \ldots \ldots \ldots \ldots \ldots \ldots \ldots \ldots \ldots \ldots \\
\chi^n(\overset{o}{x}{}^1, \overset{o}{x}{}^2, \overset{o}{x}{}^3, \ldots, \overset{o}{x}{}^n, \overset{o}{t}, t) \equiv \chi^n(\overset{o}{x}{}^2, \overset{o}{x}{}^1, \overset{o}{x}{}^3, \ldots, \overset{o}{x}{}^n, \overset{o}{t}, t),
\end{cases}
$$

where $\chi(\overset{o}{x}, \overset{o}{t}, t)$ denotes the solution vector of the equations of motion. First, the equations are correct if $t = \overset{o}{t}$. Further, the right-hand sides fulfil the differential equations for the corresponding left-hand sides, as we shall show now for the first and the last equations,

$$
\dot{\chi}^2(\overset{o}{x}{}^2, \overset{o}{x}{}^1, \overset{o}{x}{}^3, \ldots, \overset{o}{x}{}^n, \overset{o}{t}, t) -
$$
$$
- X^1\{\chi^2(\overset{o}{x}{}^2, \overset{o}{x}{}^1, \ldots), \chi^1(\overset{o}{x}{}^2, \overset{o}{x}{}^1, \ldots), \chi^3(\overset{o}{x}{}^2, \overset{o}{x}{}^1, \ldots), \ldots\}
$$

$$
\equiv \dot{\chi}^2(\overset{o}{x}{}^2, \overset{o}{x}{}^1, \overset{o}{x}{}^3, \ldots, t) -
$$
$$
- X^2\{\chi^1(\overset{o}{x}{}^2, \overset{o}{x}{}^1, \ldots), \chi^2(\overset{o}{x}{}^2, \overset{o}{x}{}^1, \ldots), \chi^3(\overset{o}{x}{}^2, \overset{o}{x}{}^1, \ldots), \ldots\}
$$

$$
\equiv 0,
$$

and, similarly,

$$\dot{\chi}^n(\overset{\scriptscriptstyle 0}{x}{}^2, \overset{\scriptscriptstyle 0}{x}{}^1, \ldots) -$$
$$- X^n\{\chi^2(\overset{\scriptscriptstyle 0}{x}{}^2, \overset{\scriptscriptstyle 0}{x}{}^1, \ldots), \ \chi^1(\overset{\scriptscriptstyle 0}{x}{}^2, \overset{\scriptscriptstyle 0}{x}{}^1, \ldots), \ \chi^3(\overset{\scriptscriptstyle 0}{x}{}^2, \overset{\scriptscriptstyle 0}{x}{}^1, \ldots), \ \ldots\}$$
$$\equiv \dot{\chi}^n(\overset{\scriptscriptstyle 0}{x}{}^2, \overset{\scriptscriptstyle 0}{x}{}^1, \ldots) -$$
$$- X^n\{\chi^1(\overset{\scriptscriptstyle 0}{x}{}^2, \overset{\scriptscriptstyle 0}{x}{}^1, \ldots), \ \chi^2(\overset{\scriptscriptstyle 0}{x}{}^2, \overset{\scriptscriptstyle 0}{x}{}^1, \ldots), \ \chi^3(\overset{\scriptscriptstyle 0}{x}{}^2, \overset{\scriptscriptstyle 0}{x}{}^1, \ldots), \ \ldots\}$$
$$\equiv 0.$$

The uniqueness theorem 6.2 now proves the stated symmetry of the solution vector $\chi(\overset{\scriptscriptstyle 0}{x}, \overset{\scriptscriptstyle 0}{t}, t)$. The symmetry of $w(x, t)$ is demonstrated in this way:

$$w(x^1, x^2, x^3, \ldots, x^n, t)$$
$$\equiv \overset{\scriptscriptstyle 0}{w}\{\chi^1(x^1, x^2, \ldots, x^n, t, \overset{\scriptscriptstyle 0}{t}) \, \chi^2(x^1, x^2, \ldots), \ \ldots, \ \chi^n(x^1, \ldots)\}$$
$$\text{(by Theorem 17.1),}$$
$$\equiv \overset{\scriptscriptstyle 0}{w}\{\chi^2(x^2, x^1, \ldots), \ \chi^1(x^2, x^1, \ldots), \ \chi^3(x^2, x^1, \ldots), \ \ldots\}$$
$$\equiv \overset{\scriptscriptstyle 0}{w}\{\chi^1(x^2, x^1, \ldots), \ \chi^2(x^2, x^1, \ldots), \ \chi^3(x^2, x^1, \ldots), \ \ldots\}$$
$$\text{(by the symmetry of } \overset{\scriptscriptstyle 0}{w}),$$
$$\equiv w(x^2, x^1, x^3, \ldots, x^n, t).$$
$$\text{Q.E.D.}$$

17.8. DEFINITIONS. Let a system of mass-points consist of a classes of equivalent mass-points. Denote by $w^{(\alpha)}(x^\alpha, t)$ the probability density of the particles of class α in a phase space $\Gamma^{(\alpha)}$ common to them all, and denote by $m^{(\alpha)}$ and $n^{(\alpha)}$ their masses and their number. Position vectors in the real space R^3 are denoted by $q' = (q_1', q_2', q_3')$, the corresponding momenta are $p' = (p_1', p_2', p_3')$, the set of all q' is Γ_q', the set of all p' is Γ_p'. Velocity vectors will be denoted by $u = (u_1, u_2, u_3)$. Then the *number density* $D^{(\alpha)}(q', t)$ of the class α is defined by

$$D^{(\alpha)}(q', t) \equiv n^{(\alpha)} \int_{\Gamma_p'} w^{(\alpha)}(p', q', t) \, \mathrm{d}p',$$

its *mass density* $\rho^{(\alpha)}(q', t)$ is defined by

$$\rho^{(\alpha)}(q', t) \equiv m^{(\alpha)} n^{(\alpha)} \int_{\Gamma_p'} w^{(\alpha)}(p', q', t) \, \mathrm{d}p',$$

its *mean velocity* or *streaming velocity* $\bar{u}_\lambda^{(\alpha)}(q',t)$ is defined by

$$\bar{u}_\lambda^{(\alpha)}(q',t) \equiv \frac{\displaystyle\int_{\Gamma_{p'}} u_\lambda\, w^{(\alpha)}(p',q',t)\,\mathrm{d}p'}{\displaystyle\int_{\Gamma_{p'}} w^{(\alpha)}(p',q',t)\,\mathrm{d}p'}$$

(i.e. it is the conditional expectation value of the velocity with respect to the position q'; cf. § 16.3), and the tensor of its *partial pressure* $P_{\kappa\lambda}^{(\alpha)}(q',t)$ is defined by

$$P_{\kappa\lambda}^{(\alpha)}(q',t) \equiv \rho^{(\alpha)}\overline{(u_\kappa - \bar{u}_\kappa^{(\alpha)})\,(u_\lambda - \bar{u}_\lambda^{(\alpha)})}^{(\alpha)}$$

$$\equiv \rho^{(\alpha)}\frac{\displaystyle\int_{\Gamma_{p'}} (u_\kappa - \bar{u}_\kappa^{(\alpha)})\,(u_\lambda - \bar{u}_\lambda^{(\alpha)})\, w^{(\alpha)}(p',q',t)\,\mathrm{d}p'}{\displaystyle\int_{\Gamma_{p'}} w^{(\alpha)}(p',q',t)\,\mathrm{d}p'}.$$

Note. In order not to interrupt the present train of thought, we postpone the discussion of the relation between the quantities just defined and the corresponding phenomenological quantities until § 22. At present, we content ourselves with the observation that, in the following theorems, the statistically defined quantities play a role similar to that of the phenomenological quantities in the corresponding theorems of hydromechanics.

17.9. CONTINUITY THEOREM OF HYDROMECHANICS. *Suppose that for a system of mass-points the assumptions of Theorem 17.5 hold. Then the mass density $\rho^{(\alpha)}(q',t)$ and the streaming velocity $\bar{u}^{(\alpha)}(q',t)$ of the class α of equivalent particles satisfy the equation*

$$\frac{\partial \rho^{(\alpha)}}{\partial t} + \sum_{\lambda=1}^{3} \frac{\partial}{\partial q'_\lambda}(\rho^{(\alpha)}\,\bar{u}_\lambda^{(\alpha)}) = 0.$$

Proof. Integrate the equation of Theorem 17.5 over Γ_p^λ (i.e. over the set of all vectors p^λ), after having introduced the explicit expression for H^λ into it. All the terms which contain the potential vanish since $w(x,t)$ vanishes for large values of $|x|$. Now, by a suitable change of notation, the equation of the theorem is obtained.

17.10. EULER'S EQUATIONS OF HYDROMECHANICS. *Under the assumptions of Theorem 17.5 the following equations hold, for each class* α *of equivalent particles:*

$$\frac{\partial \bar{u}_\iota^{(\alpha)}}{\partial t} + \sum_{\kappa=1}^{3} \frac{\partial \bar{u}_\iota^{(\alpha)}}{\partial q_\kappa'}\, \bar{u}_\kappa^{(\alpha)}$$

$$= -\frac{1}{m^{(\alpha)}}\frac{\partial U^{(\alpha)}}{\partial q_\iota'} - \frac{1}{\rho^{(\alpha)}}\sum_{\kappa=1}^{3}\frac{\partial P_{\iota\kappa}^{(\alpha)}}{\partial q_\kappa'} - \frac{n^{(\alpha)}}{\rho^{(\alpha)}}\sum_{\nu=1}^{n}\int_{\Gamma^\nu}\frac{\partial V^{\alpha\nu}}{\partial q_\iota'}\int_{\Gamma_{p'}}\omega^{\alpha\nu}\,\mathrm{d}p'\,\mathrm{d}x^\nu,$$

$$\iota = 1, 2, 3,$$

where $\quad U^{(\alpha)}(q',t) \equiv V^\alpha(q',t) + \sum_{\nu=1}^{n}\int_{\Gamma^\nu} V^{\alpha\nu}(q',q^\nu,t)\,w^\nu(x^\nu,t)\,\mathrm{d}x^\nu.$

Here, for convenient notation, it is supposed that the class α contains the αth particle.

Proof. Write the equation of Theorem 17.5 as equation for the class α, multiply by $n^{(\alpha)}\, m^{(\alpha)}\, u_\iota = n^{(\alpha)}\, p_\iota'$ and integrate over Γ_p'. By Definitions 17.8 and by means of a partial integration of the third term, we obtain

$$\frac{\partial}{\partial t}\left(\rho^{(\alpha)}\,\bar{u}_\iota^{(\alpha)}\right) + \sum_{\kappa=1}^{3}\frac{\partial}{\partial q_\kappa'}\left(\rho^{(\alpha)}\,\overline{u_\iota\, u_\kappa}^{(\alpha)}\right) + \frac{\rho^{(\alpha)}}{m^{(\alpha)}}\frac{\partial U^{(\alpha)}}{\partial q_\iota'}$$

$$= \sum_{\nu=1}^{n}\sum_{\kappa=1}^{3}\int_{\Gamma^\nu}\frac{\partial V^{\alpha\nu}}{\partial q_\kappa'}\int_{\Gamma_{p'}}\frac{\partial \omega^{\alpha\nu}}{\partial p_\kappa'}\,p_\iota'\,n^{(\alpha)}\,\mathrm{d}p'\,\mathrm{d}x^\nu.$$

The two first terms are transformed in the following fashion:

$$\frac{\partial}{\partial t}\left(\rho^{(\alpha)}\,\bar{u}_\iota^{(\alpha)}\right) + \sum_{\kappa=1}^{3}\frac{\partial}{\partial q_\kappa'}\left(\rho^{(\alpha)}\,\overline{u_\iota\, u_\kappa}^{(\alpha)}\right)$$

$$= \frac{\partial \bar{u}_\iota^{(\alpha)}}{\partial t}\,\rho^{(\alpha)} + \bar{u}_\iota^{(\alpha)}\frac{\partial \rho^{(\alpha)}}{\partial t} + \sum_{\kappa=1}^{3}\frac{\partial}{\partial q_\kappa'}\left(\rho^{(\alpha)}\,\overline{u_\iota\, u_\kappa}^{(\alpha)}\right)$$

$$= \rho^{(\alpha)}\frac{\partial \bar{u}_\iota^{(\alpha)}}{\partial t} - \bar{u}_\iota^{(\alpha)}\sum_{\kappa=1}^{3}\frac{\partial}{\partial q_\kappa'}\left(\rho^{(\alpha)}\,\bar{u}_\iota^{(\alpha)}\right) + \sum_{\kappa=1}^{3}\frac{\partial}{\partial q_\kappa'}\left(\rho^{(\alpha)}\, u_\iota\,\overline{u u_\kappa}^{(\alpha)}\right)$$

$$\text{(by Theorem 17.9)}$$

$$= \rho^{(\alpha)}\frac{\partial \bar{u}_\iota^{(\alpha)}}{\partial t} - \sum_{\kappa=1}^{3}\left\{\frac{\partial}{\partial q_\kappa'}\left(\rho^{(\alpha)}\bar{u}_\kappa^{(\alpha)}\,\bar{u}_\iota^{(\alpha)}\right) - \rho^{(\alpha)}\bar{u}_\kappa^{(\alpha)}\frac{\partial \bar{u}_\iota^{(\alpha)}}{\partial q_\kappa'}\right\} +$$

$$+ \sum_{\kappa=1}^{3}\frac{\partial}{\partial q_\kappa'}\left(\rho^{(\alpha)}\,\overline{u_\kappa\, u_\iota}^{(\alpha)}\right)$$

$$= \rho^{(\alpha)}\frac{\partial \bar{u}_\iota^{(\alpha)}}{\partial t} + \rho^{(\alpha)}\sum_{\kappa=1}^{3}\frac{\partial \bar{u}_\iota^{(\alpha)}}{\partial q_\kappa'}\,\bar{u}_\kappa^{(\alpha)} + \sum_{\kappa=1}^{3}\frac{\partial}{\partial q_\kappa'}\left\{\rho^\alpha\overline{(u_\iota - \bar{u}_\iota^{(\alpha)})\,(u_\kappa - \bar{u}_\kappa^{(\alpha)})}^{(\alpha)}\right\}.$$

Finally, by a partial integration of the last term, the equations of the theorem are obtained.

Notes. The equations of the theorem differ from Euler's equations of phenomenological hydromechanics in three respects:
  (i) Instead of a scalar pressure, there is a pressure tensor.
  (ii) The pressure tensor does not represent the total pressure, but only the partial pressure of the class α. Similarly, only the partial density enters the equations.
  (iii) There are additional terms containing the functions $\omega^{\alpha\nu}$. It cannot be concluded that these last terms are small simply because they do not occur in phenomenological hydromechanics. It is conceivable that in the interior of the system (the "fluid") their sum is approximately equal to zero without the single terms necessarily vanishing. Near the boundary of the system the situation is different: the distribution of the forces acting on the particles deviates here considerably from spherical symmetry so that the single terms of the sum no longer cancel each other. Thus these additional terms are probably of importance in the interpretation of such phenomena as evaporation or surface tension.

So far, only "monatomic molecules" have been dealt with. Systems consisting of "multiatomic molecules" can be investigated in a similar fashion, on the general base of Theorem 17.4 and Corollary 17.4. Thus, for instance, for systems of two-atomic molecules an equation for $w^{\kappa\lambda}(x^{\kappa}, x^{\lambda}, t)$ can be established, which corresponds to the equation of Theorem 17.5, etc.

§ 18. The initial value problem

18.1. The problem of calculating the probability density $w'(x', t)$ of the component x' at time t' in its phase space Γ' from a given initial probability density $w'(x', \overset{\circ}{t}) \equiv \overset{\circ}{w}'(x')$ at time $\overset{\circ}{t}$ was encountered in § 16.5. There was the difficulty that the coefficients of the equation for $w'(x', t)$ could be determined only if the probability density $w(x, t)$ in Γ was already known—which was not the case. In order to find a suitable approach towards a solution of the problem, we considered, in § 17, particular cases, namely Hamiltonian systems and systems of mass-points. Thus, for example, for systems of equivalent particles, the following equation was obtained:

$$\frac{\partial w^1}{\partial t} + \sum_{\kappa=1}^{3}\left(\frac{\partial w^1}{\partial q^1_\kappa}\frac{\partial H^1}{\partial p^1_\kappa} - \frac{\partial w^1}{\partial p^1_\kappa}\frac{\partial H^1}{\partial q^1_\kappa}\right) = (n-1)\sum_{\kappa=1}^{3}\int_{\Gamma^2}\frac{\partial V^{12}}{\partial q^1_\kappa}\frac{\partial \omega^{12}}{\partial p^1_\kappa}\,\mathrm{d}x^2. \quad (*)$$

(See Theorem 17.5.) Here, the functions $\partial H^1/\partial p_\kappa^1$, $\partial H^1/\partial q_\kappa^1$ themselves depend on the function w^1: to any function w^1 there correspond certain functions $\partial H^1/\partial p_\kappa^1$, $\partial H^1/\partial q_\kappa'$ which are uniquely determined; that is, they are functions in the general sense of § 3, the arguments of which are functions in the usual particular sense of analysis (i.e. they are scalar functions, defined in certain vector spaces). Briefly, we say: $\partial H^1/\partial p_\kappa^1$ and $\partial H^1/\partial q_\kappa^1$ are *transforms* of w^1.

The function ω^{12} is a transform of the function w^{12}, but not of w^1. Now, without any difficulty, a differential equation can be established also for the function w^{12}, by Theorem 17.4. But a new unknown function appears in it, namely, $w^{123}(x^1, x^2, x^3, t)$, which is not a transform of w^{12}, etc. Again, it seems that $w^1(x^1, t)$ can be determined only if $w(x, t)$ is already known.

In a strict sense, this is correct. Nevertheless, in order to be able to work in spaces of small numbers of dimensions, we introduce the *fictitious assumption* that w^{12} is yet a transform of w^1. We say "fiction", and do not say "hypothesis", since the assumption is certainly wrong. For there is always an infinite number of initial probability densities $\overset{\circ}{w}(x)$ in Γ such that all the corresponding probability densities in Γ^1 coincide with any given function $\overset{\circ}{w}^1(x^1)$; hence there is also an infinite number of different functions $w^{12}(x^1, x^2, t)$ corresponding to different densities $\overset{\circ}{w}(x)$, but to the same density $\overset{\circ}{w}^1(x^1)$.

To construct such densities $\overset{\circ}{w}(x)$, consider any non-negative symmetrical function $S(u_1, u_2, ..., u_n)$ of the n-independent variables $u_1, u_2, ..., u_n$, for instance a suitable symmetrical polynomial, and put

$$\overset{\circ}{w}(x) = S\{\overset{\circ}{w}^1(x^1), \overset{\circ}{w}^2(x^1), ..., \overset{\circ}{w}^x(x^n)\}.$$

The function S has to satisfy only two conditions, namely,

$$\overset{\circ}{w}^1(x^1) \equiv \int_{\Gamma/\Gamma^1} S\{\overset{\circ}{w}^1(x^1), ..., \overset{\circ}{w}^n(x^n)\}\,\mathrm{d}(x/x^1),$$

and the condition of normalization

$$\int_\Gamma S\{\overset{\circ}{w}^1(x^1), ..., \overset{\circ}{w}^n(x^n)\}\,\mathrm{d}x = 1.$$

By assuming an expression for S which contains at least three arbitrary parameters, both the conditions can be fulfilled by an infinite variety of densities $\overset{\circ}{w}$.

Only those fictions are admissible, of course, which yield acceptable approximations to reality, either always or in most cases or, at least, in the cases which are most important in practice. If, for example, there seems to be sufficient reason for the assumption that, on the whole, the motions of any two particles are nearly independent of each other, the hypothesis that $w^{12} \approx w^1 w^2$ appears plausible and, therefore, the fiction that $\omega^{12} \equiv 0$ is worth while trying. This case occurs when the magnitude of the force exerted by any particle on the first particle (say) is, "on the average", "in general", etc., much smaller than the total force exerted by all the other particles on the first mass-point. This assumption has been made frequently in the mechanics of stellar systems. The theory of fluids can be based on the equation for w^{12} where a plausible fiction about w^{123} as a transform of w^{12} has to be introduced, etc.

The general type of all these equations reads

$$\frac{\partial v}{\partial t} + \sum_{\nu=1}^{n} \frac{\partial v}{\partial x_\nu} X_\nu(v, t) = Y(v, t) \qquad (**)$$

where $X_\nu(v, t)$ and $Y(v, t)$ are transforms of the function v which may depend on the time variable t. The function $v(x, t)$ depends on the variables $x = (x_1, ..., x_n)$ and t. Its initial "value" $v(x, \overset{\circ}{t}) \equiv \overset{\circ}{v}(x)$ at time $\overset{\circ}{t}$ is supposed to be given. The subject of this section is the initial value problem: to determine the solution v of equation (**) which takes the initial value $\overset{\circ}{v}$ at time $\overset{\circ}{t}$. First, particular cases will be considered.

18.2. DEFINITIONS. A linear space R (cf. § 5.1) is said to be *metric(al)* if, for each element f of R, there is a *"norm"* $\|f\|$, i.e. a non-negative number such that

(i) $$\|\alpha f\| = |\alpha| \, \|f\|$$

for every real number α,

(ii) $$f = 0 \quad \text{if} \quad \|f\| = 0,$$

(iii) $$\|f_1 + f_2\| \leqslant \|f_1\| + \|f_2\|,$$

for every pair of elements f_1, f_2 of R. (Triangular inequality, cf. § 4.10.)

A metric linear space R is said to be *complete* if every "Cauchy sequence" of elements of R converges towards an element of R (cf. § 9.1). A complete metric linear space is called a *Banach space*.

Continuity, differentiability and (Riemann) integrability with respect to a (one-dimensional) real variable can be defined for the elements of a Banach space in a manner similar to that in which these concepts are applied to real functions of a real variable, and are governed by similar laws.

Examples. Hilbert spaces are Banach spaces. The following theorem yields a second example.

18.3. THEOREM. *Let B be a bounded closed subset of R^n. Then the set C of all the functions $f(x)$ which are continuous in B is a Banach space if the norm $\|f\|$ is defined by*

$$\|f\| = \max_{x \in B} f(x).$$

Proof. For each function $f(x)$, there is a maximum of $|f(x)|$ in B, as is demonstrated indirectly. From

$$\max (f+g) \leqslant \max f + \max g$$

it follows that C is a metric linear space. For a Cauchy sequence of elements $f_1, f_2, \ldots$ of R, the sequence of real numbers $f_1(x), f_2(x), \ldots$, for any particular point x of B, converges towards a number $f(x)$, by Cauchy's convergence theorem. The function $f(x)$ is continuous in B since, for any two points x and x' of B,

$$|f(x')-f(x)| \leqslant |f(x')-f_\lambda(x')| + |f_\lambda(x')-f_\lambda(x)| + |f_\lambda(x)-f(x)|,$$

and the right-hand side is, for sufficiently large indices and sufficiently small distances $|x'-x|$, arbitrarily small. Thus the function $f(x)$ is an element of C, i.e. the metric linear space C is complete.

                                                                    Q.E.D.

18.4. THEOREM. *Let $Y(f, t)$ be a transform (i.e. a function in the general sense of § 3) of the elements of a Banach space R into elements of R, which depends on the time variable t. Let*

T denote the time interval $\overset{0}{t} \leqslant t \leqslant \overset{1}{t}$, and K be the set of all elements f of R such that

$$\|f - \overset{0}{v}\| \leqslant c$$

where $\overset{0}{v}$ is any fixed element of R and c any positive number. Suppose that for all pairs of elements f, f' of K and all instants t of T a Lipschitz condition holds, namely

$$\| Y(f', t) - Y(f, t) \| \leqslant N \|f' - f\|,$$

where N denotes a positive constant which may depend on the set $K \times T$. Finally, let M be a positive constant such that

$$\| Y(f, t) \| \leqslant M$$

for all elements f of K and all instants t of T. Then the differential equation

$$\frac{dv}{dt} = Y(v, t)$$

possesses, in the time interval

$$\overset{0}{t} \leqslant t \leqslant t_1 = \min\left(\overset{1}{t}, \overset{0}{t} + \frac{c}{M}\right),$$

exactly one solution $v(\overset{0}{v}, \overset{0}{t}, t)$ which satisfies the initial condition

$$v(\overset{0}{v}, \overset{0}{t}, \overset{0}{t}) = \overset{0}{v}.$$

The solution can be constructed by means of the iterative scheme

$$v_0 = \overset{0}{v}, \quad v_{\lambda+1} = \overset{0}{v} + \int_{t^0}^{t} Y[v_\lambda(\overset{0}{v}, \overset{0}{t}, \tau), \tau] \, d\tau, \quad \lambda = 0, 1, 2, \ldots,$$

and depends on $\overset{0}{v}$ continuously.

The proof is analogous to the proofs of Theorems 6.2 and 6.4.

Note. In applying this theorem to suitable particular cases of equation (*) of § 18.1, it is to be observed that the assumptions of the theorem must be satisfied by the transformations $\partial\omega^{12}/\partial p_x^1$ or, rather, the right-hand side of equation (*) and not only by the transform ω^{12}.

COROLLARY. Assume that, for the transformation $Y(f, t)$, there is a Lipschitz constant N which is common to all sets $K \times T$. Then the solution $v(\overset{0}{v}, \overset{0}{t}, t)$ of the differential equation $\overset{0}{v} = Y(v, t)$ can be extended to every instant t.

The proof is analogous to that of Theorem 6.3.

18.5. The initial value problem

$$\frac{\partial v}{\partial t} + \sum_{\nu=1}^{n} \frac{\partial v}{\partial x_\nu} X_\nu(v, t) = 0, \quad v(x, \overset{0}{t}) \equiv \overset{0}{v}(x), \qquad (*)$$

where $v(x, t)$ denotes a (scalar) function defined in R^{n+1} and the X_ν's are transforms, can be formulated, by means of Theorem 17.3, in the following fashion. Let $v(x, t)$ be a solution of

$$\frac{\partial v}{\partial t} + \sum_{1}^{n} \frac{\partial v}{\partial x_\nu} g_\nu(x, t) = 0$$

satisfying the initial condition $v(x, \overset{0}{t}) = \overset{0}{v}(x)$; let $g_\nu(x, t) \equiv H_\nu(v, t)$; and let $\psi(\overset{0}{x}, \overset{0}{t}, t)$ be the solution of the system of ordinary differential equations $\dot{x} = g(x, t)$ such that $\psi(\overset{0}{x}, \overset{0}{t}, \overset{0}{t}) = \overset{0}{x}$. Then

$$v(x, t) \equiv \overset{0}{v}\{\psi(x, t, \overset{0}{t})\}.$$

The vector $g(x, t)$ is a transform $Y(\psi, t)$ of the vector $\psi(\overset{0}{x}, \overset{0}{t}, t)$, and this vector is the solution of the initial value problem

$$\frac{\partial \psi}{\partial t} = Y(\psi, t), \quad \psi(\overset{0}{x}, \overset{0}{t}, \overset{0}{t}) = \overset{0}{x}. \qquad (**)$$

Under suitable assumptions about the initial condition $\overset{0}{v}(x)$ and the transforms X_ν, the problem $(**)$ can be regarded as a particular case of the problem dealt with in § 18.4, if the corresponding Banach space is that described in Theorem 18.3. If, conversely, ψ is a solution of $(**)$, then $\overset{0}{v}\{\psi(x, t, \overset{0}{t})\}$ is a solution of $(*)$. Hence the problems $(*)$ and $(**)$ are equivalent, and thus both can be solved by the method of § 18.4.

That method may be altered, for the present problem, in the following manner. Define an infinite sequence of functions $v_0(x, t), v_1(x, t), v_2(x, t)$ successively by the iterative scheme

$$\left\{ \begin{array}{c} v_0(x, t) \equiv \overset{0}{v}(x), \\[2mm] \dfrac{\partial v_{\lambda+1}}{\partial t} + \sum_{\nu=1}^{n} \dfrac{\partial v_{\lambda+1}}{\partial x_\nu} X_\nu(v_\lambda, t) = 0, \\[2mm] v_\lambda(x, \overset{0}{t}) \equiv \overset{0}{v}(x). \end{array} \right\} \quad \lambda = 0, 1, 2, \dots .$$

Under suitable assumptions about the initial condition and the transformations (such as boundedness, Lipschitz inequality, etc.), there is, for each value of λ, a uniquely determined function v_λ, according to Theorem 17.3. The sequence $v_0, v_1, v_2, \dots$

can be shown to converge towards a solution of the problem, and this is its only solution.

18.6. The solution of the general initial value problem

$$\frac{\partial v}{\partial t} + \sum_{\nu=1}^{n} \frac{\partial v}{\partial x_\nu} X_\nu(v,t) = Y(v,t), \quad v(x,\overset{0}{t}) = \overset{0}{v}(x) \qquad (*)$$

can be founded on the following generalization of Theorem 17.3.

THEOREM. *Let the function* $h(x,t)$ *possess continuous derivatives with respect to* $x_1, x_2, \ldots, x_n$, *for all values of* (x,t). *Then, under the assumptions and with the notation of Theorem* 17.3, *the initial value problem*

$$\frac{\partial v}{\partial t} + \sum_{\nu=1}^{n} \frac{\partial v}{\partial x_\nu} g_\nu(x,t) = h(x,t), \quad v(x,\overset{0}{t}) = \overset{0}{v}(x)$$

possesses a uniquely determined solution $v(x,t)$, *which is given by*

$$v(x,t) \equiv \overset{0}{v}\{\psi(x,t,\overset{0}{t})\} + \int_{\overset{0}{t}}^{t} h\{\psi(x,t,\tau),\tau\}\,d\tau.$$

Proof. That the expression given for $v(x,t)$ is indeed a solution of the problem is demonstrated by inserting it into the equation. If there were a second solution $\bar{v}(x,t)$, the difference $\bar{v} - v$ would be a solution of the initial value problem

$$\frac{\partial}{\partial t}(\bar{v}-v) + \sum_{\nu=1}^{n} g_\nu \frac{\partial}{\partial x_\nu}(\bar{v}-v) = 0, \quad \bar{v}(x,\overset{0}{t}) - v(x,\overset{0}{t}) \equiv 0.$$

Hence, by Theorem 17.3,

$$\bar{v}(x,t) - v(x,t) \equiv 0. \qquad \text{Q.E.D.}$$

Now problem (*) can be solved by a method similar to that expounded in § 18.4. Define an infinite sequence of functions

$$v_0(x,t), v_1(x,t), v_2(x,t), \ldots$$

by the iterative scheme

$$\left\{\begin{array}{c} v_0(x,t) \equiv \overset{0}{v}(x), \\ \dfrac{\partial v_{\lambda+1}}{\partial t} + \sum_\nu \dfrac{\partial v_{\lambda+1}}{\partial x_\nu} X_\nu(v_\lambda,t) = Y(v_\lambda,t), \\ v_\lambda(x,t) \equiv \overset{0}{v}(x). \end{array}\right\} \quad \lambda = 0,1,2,\ldots.$$

Under certain assumptions about boundedness, Lipschitz

condition, etc., the sequence converges towards a solution of the problem, which, in fact, is unique.

This is the basic idea of the method. As to the conditions which are sufficient to guarantee its proper working, the reader may be referred to the literature.

§ 19. The approach of mechanical systems towards states of statistical equilibrium

19.1. In many mechanical processes or, rather, processes which are interpreted mechanically (as, for example, the passage of a compressed gas into an empty vessel) the systems approach towards macroscopically stationary states, i.e. towards states in which no changes can be observed in course of time. In such a case it seems plausible to attribute a probability distribution which does not depend on the time. For this assumption to be justified, it is necessary that the approach towards the stationary state should actually have been observed. This means that the initial and final macroscopic states of the system are different, and that the system remains in the final state, after having reached it, through all the subsequent time. If, on the other hand, during the whole period of observation, no change in the macroscopic state of the system can be observed, the system may, but need not, be in a state of "statistical equilibrium" (cf. Definition 19.2). There can be actual essential changes of its state, which are only unmeasurably slow from a human point of view, but may be quite rapid if measured in a *time scale* which is appropriate for the system. This is true, for example, for stellar systems. Instead of a formal definition of the concept of the time scale, an illustration will be given now which, it is hoped, will make the notion clear.

Example. A system of n gravitating mass-points of masses $m^1, m^2, ..., m^n$ and position vectors $q^1, q^2, ..., q^n$ is governed by the equations of motion

$$\ddot{q}^i = G \sum_{i \neq j} m^j \frac{q^j - q^i}{|q^j - q^i|}, \quad i = 1, ..., n,$$

where G is the constant of gravitation. Now introduce non-dimensional masses $\tilde{m}^i$, position vectors $\tilde{q}^i$ and time variable $\tilde{t}$

by the following equations

$$\left.\begin{array}{l} m^i = M\tilde{m}^i, \\ q^i = L\tilde{q}^i, \\ t = T\tilde{t}, \end{array}\right\}$$

where

$$M = \sum_{j=1}^{n} m^j$$

and L and T are positive constants of dimensions of length and time. Then, in the non-dimensional quantities, the equations of motion read

$$\frac{\mathrm{d}^2 \tilde{q}^i}{\mathrm{d}\tilde{t}^2} = \frac{GMT^2}{L^3} \sum_{i \neq j} \tilde{m}^j \frac{\tilde{q}^j - \tilde{q}^i}{|\tilde{q}^j - \tilde{q}^i|}, \qquad i = 1, 2, ..., n.$$

During the period $0 \leqslant \tilde{t} \leqslant 1$, the magnitudes of the velocity vectors $\mathrm{d}\tilde{q}^i/\mathrm{d}\tilde{t}^i$ change, on the average, by quantities of the order 1 if for L the average distance of any two particles is taken and the value of T is chosen in such a fashion that the "non-dimensional constant of gravitation" GMT^2/L^3 adopts the value 1. So, during the same time interval, the velocity vectors $\mathrm{d}\tilde{q}^i/\mathrm{d}t$ and the position vectors $\tilde{q}^i$ will be of order 1 if the initial velocities are also, at most, of this order. The value of T, arising from the above stipulation, is the time scale of the system. Thus,

$$T = \sqrt{\frac{L^3}{GM}}.$$

It seems that an eventual approach of a system towards a stationary state can be observed at the earliest after a period of observation which is of the order of the time scale (unless the non-dimensional initial velocities are, in magnitude, considerably larger than unity; but then it appears doubtful whether such an approach may be expected at all).

19.2. DEFINITION. A mechanical system is said to be in (a state of) *statistical equilibrium* or in a *statistically stationary state* if the observations of it can be described by means of a probability density $w(x)$ in the phase space Γ, which does not depend on the time.

Note. The word "state" is used in several different senses. The microscopic state of the system is described by its phase vector x, according to § 10.1; the macroscopic state is what is actually observed; the expression "state of statistical equilibrium" refers to the probability distribution of the phase-point x and is thus, in a sense, intermediate between the microscopic and the macroscopic notions.

19.3. THEOREM. *For a mechanical system with stationary measure-conserving phase flow* χ, *a probability density* $w(x)$ *which is independent of the time is possible* (i.e. the assumption of its existence does not imply a self-contradiction) *if and only if there is a (Lebesgue-measurable) invariant subset* J *of the phase space* Γ *of positive finite measure* μJ.

Proof. Assume that there is an invariant subset J of positive finite measure μJ, and let $\delta_J(x)$ be its characteristic function. Then the function $\delta_J(x)/\mu J$ is formally admissible as a probability density.

Conversely, let a probability $w(x)$ be given. Now define sets J_λ where $\lambda = 0, 1, 2, \ldots$ such that J_λ consists of all the points x of Γ for which $\lambda \leqslant w(x) < \lambda + 1$. By § 8.4, J_λ is measurable and invariant. From

$$1 = \int_\Gamma w(x)\,dx = \sum_{\lambda=0}^\infty \int_{J_\lambda} w(x)\,dx,$$

it follows that
$$1 \geqslant \sum_{\lambda=0}^\infty \lambda.\mu J_\lambda = \sum_{\lambda=1}^\infty \lambda.\mu J_\lambda.$$

Hence
$$\mu J_\lambda \leqslant \frac{1}{\lambda}, \quad \text{for} \quad \lambda = 1, 2, \ldots.$$

Either at least one of the measures $\mu J_1, \mu J_2, \ldots$ is positive—in which case the statement of the theorem is proved—or they all vanish. In this case

$$\int_{J_0} w(x)\,dx = 1.$$

Now define sets i_λ, $\lambda = 1, 2, \ldots$, such that i_λ consists of all the points x for which $1/\lambda > w(x) \geqslant 1/(\lambda+1)$, and let i_0 be the set of all x for which $w(x) = 0$. All these sets are measurable and invariant, too. From

$$1 = \int_{J_0} w(x)\,dx = \int_{i_0} w(x)\,dx + \sum_{\lambda=1}^\infty \int_{i_\lambda} w(x)\,dx = \sum_{\lambda=1}^\infty \int_{i_\lambda} w(x)\,dx,$$

it now follows that

$$\sum_{\lambda=1}^{\infty} \frac{\mu i_\lambda}{\lambda+1} \leqslant 1 \leqslant \sum_{\lambda=1}^{\infty} \frac{\mu i_\lambda}{\lambda}.$$

Therefore all the measures μi_λ are finite and at least one of them is positive.

Q.E.D.

COROLLARY. *There are systems with stationary measure-conserving phase flows for which there is no invariant subset of the phase space of positive finite measure and, therefore, no state of statistical equilibrium.*

Example. The mechanical system with the equations of motion

$$\left.\begin{aligned} \dot{x}_1 &= x_2, \\ \dot{x}_2 &= x_1, \end{aligned}\right\}$$

possesses a Hamiltonian function, namely, $H(x) \equiv \frac{1}{2}(x_1^2 - x_2^2)$. Hence its phase flow is measure-conserving and since $H(x)$ does not depend on the time variable, stationary. The general solution of the equations of motion reads

$$\left.\begin{aligned} x_1 &= \chi_1(\overset{\circ}{x}, t) = \overset{\circ}{x}_1 \cosh t + \overset{\circ}{x}_2 \sinh t, \\ x_2 &= \chi_2(\overset{\circ}{x}, t) = \overset{\circ}{x}_1 \sinh t + \overset{\circ}{x}_2 \cosh t. \end{aligned}\right\}$$

Now let $\overset{\circ}{L}$ be any bounded Lebesgue subset of Γ such that $|\overset{\circ}{x}_1 + \overset{\circ}{x}_2| \geqslant \epsilon = \text{const.} > 0$ for all the points $\overset{\circ}{x}$ of $\overset{\circ}{L}$. Then $|\chi(\overset{\circ}{x}, t)|$ tends towards ∞ if $t \to \infty$, uniformly for all points $\overset{\circ}{x}$ of $\overset{\circ}{L}$. So an increasing sequence of instants $t_1, t_2, t_3, \ldots$ can be constructed such that no two sets of the sequence

$$\chi(\overset{\circ}{L}, t_1), \chi(\overset{\circ}{L}, t_2), \chi(\overset{\circ}{L}, t_3), \ldots$$

have common points. Hence

$$\mu\chi(\overset{\circ}{L}, t_1) + \mu\chi(\overset{\circ}{L}, t_2) + \ldots = \begin{cases} 0 & \text{if} \quad \mu\overset{\circ}{L} = 0, \\ \infty & \text{if} \quad \mu\overset{\circ}{L} > 0. \end{cases}$$

In particular, this holds for a set $\overset{\circ}{L}$ which is a subset of an invariant set J. Hence either $\mu J = 0$ or $\mu J = \infty$.

Note. The objection that the above example is irrelevant for physical applications of statistical mechanics would be irrelevant itself. First, we deal here with statistical mechanics as a deductive system and not with its practical applications. Secondly, the purpose of the corollary is to emphasize the necessity of the distinction between mechanical systems according as to whether or not they admit statistically stationary states.

19.4. THEOREM. *If, for a mechanical system with a stationary measure-conserving phase flow χ, there is a continuous invariant function $F(x)$ which does not depend on the time variable and which possesses a proper relative extremum in some point a of the phase space Γ, then the system admits a probability distribution which is independent of time.*

(The word "proper" means: there is an ϵ-neighbourhood $U_\epsilon(a)$ of a in Γ such that, in the case of a minimum, say, $F(x) > F(a)$ for all the points x of $U_\epsilon(a)$ which are different from a.)

Plausible argument for the theorem. Assume that $F(x)$ has a proper minimum A in the point a and possesses continuous derivatives of second order with respect to $x_1, ..., x_n$ in a. Then, by Taylor's Theorem,

$$F(x) = A + (x-a).S(x-a) + o\{(x-a)(x-a)\}$$

where S denotes a symmetrical matrix of n lines and n columns which we suppose to be positive-definite. Approximate $F(x)$ by the two first terms. Then, for each sufficiently small positive number δ, the (open) set for which $(x-a).S(x-a) < \delta$ is invariant and has a positive finite measure.

Proof. Let ϵ be a sufficiently small positive number such that $F(x) > A$ in all the points x of the ϵ-neighbourhood $U_\epsilon(a)$ of a which are different from a. Since $F(x)$ is continuous, it takes a minimum value A' on the boundary of $U_\epsilon(a)$ which, for sufficiently small values of ϵ, is larger than A. Now denote the set of all the points x of Γ for which $F(x) < A'$ by M, and denote by D the intersection of M and $U_\epsilon(a)$. Then, it is stated, D is an invariant set of positive finite measure.

First of all, D is measurable, as the intersection of the open set M (see § 5.3) and the open set $U_\epsilon(a)$. Since $D \subseteq U_\epsilon(a)$, we have $\mu D < \infty$. Since D is open and contains the point a, it contains a neighbourhood of a, too. Hence $\mu D > 0$.

The invariance of D is demonstrated indirectly. Assume that there is a point c of D such that its image $d = \chi(c, \tau)$ at time τ

does not belong to D. Then d is a point either of $U_\varepsilon(a) - D$ or of $\Gamma - U_\varepsilon(a)$. In the first case, $F(d) \geqslant A'$ since $d \notin M$. But, for the invariance of $F(x)$, $F(d) = F(c)$, and $F(c) < A'$ since $c \in M$. Hence $F(d) < A'$. For this contradiction, d cannot belong to $U_\varepsilon(a) - D$. So assume, secondly, that $d \in \Gamma - U_\varepsilon(a)$. Then the arc $0 \leqslant t \leqslant |\tau|$ of the curve $x = \chi(c, t)$ must intersect the boundary of $U_\varepsilon(a)$ in a point e (as is easily shown by an indirect proof). Now the above inference is repeated. On the one hand, $F(e) \geqslant A'$ since e is on the boundary of $U_\varepsilon(a)$. On the other hand, $F(e) = F(c) < A'$ since $c \in M$. Hence this case is also impossible, so that $\chi(D, t) \subseteq D$ for all values of t. Therefore $\chi(D, -t) \subseteq D$, as well, and by applying the operation $\chi(\ldots, t)$ to the last inequality,

$$\chi\{\chi(D, -t), t\} \subseteq \chi(D, t) \subseteq D.$$

By § 10.3, the left-hand side is D, which, therefore, is invariant. The statement of the theorem now follows from Theorem 19.3. (The proof in the case of a maximum follows from the case just considered by letting $G(x) = -F(x)$.)

COROLLARY. *If, for a mechanical system with a time-independent Hamiltonian function, the potential function possesses a proper relative minimum, then the system admits a probability distribution which is independent of time.*

19.5. The observed approach of mechanical systems towards macroscopically stationary states seems to contradict Poincaré's Recurrence Theorem (12.2). For avoiding such a contradiction, the following interpretation of the observations is suggested. If the observed mechanical process is rapid for human concepts (cf. § 19.1), its observed properties do not correspond to its instantaneous probability density $w(x, t)$ but, instead, to an average value of $w(x, t)$ during an appropriate time interval $t_1 \ldots t_2$. Since this expression can be represented as

$$\frac{t_2}{t_2 - t_1} \cdot \frac{1}{t_2} \int_0^{t_2} w(x, t)\, dt - \frac{t_1}{t_2 - t_1} \cdot \frac{1}{t_1} \int_0^{t_1} w(x, t)\, dt,$$

the question raised by the Recurrence Theorem will be settled by an investigation of the circumstances under which the *time average*

$$\omega(x, t) \equiv \frac{1}{t} \int_0^t w(x, \tau)\, d\tau$$

of the probability density $w(x, t)$ *tends toward a time-independent density* $\omega_\infty(x)$, *as* $t \to \infty$.

THEOREM. *For a measure-conserving phase flow, the time average* $\omega(x, t)$ *of the probability density* $w(x, t)$ *satisfies the equation*

$$\int_\Gamma \omega(x, t)\, dx = 1$$

at all instants t.

Proof. By Theorem 11.5,

$$w(x, t) \equiv \overset{\circ}{w}\{\chi(x, t, 0)\},$$

where the right-hand side is integrable over Γ. The statement now follows from Theorem 13.2.

19.6. THEOREM. *Suppose that the square of the initial probability density* $\overset{\circ}{w}(x)$ *is integrable over the phase space* Γ, *and that the phase flow* χ *of the mechanical system is stationary and measure-conserving. Then there is a function* $\omega_\infty(x)$ *which is measurable in* Γ *and whose square is integrable over* Γ *such that*

$$\lim_{t \to \infty} \int \{\omega(x, t) - \omega_\infty(x)\}^2\, dx = 0,$$

where $\omega(x, t)$ *denotes the time average of the probability density* $w(x, t)$.

Proof. By §§ 17.1 and 10.3,

$$w(x, t) \equiv \overset{\circ}{w}\{\chi(x, -t)\}.$$

Hence, by § 13.1, $\omega(x, t) = \overset{\hat{\circ}}{w}(x, -t)$.

Now the theorem is obtained as a consequence of v. Neumann's Second Theorem 13.4 if $t \to -\infty$.

Note. The proof of v. Neumann's Theorem shows that the limiting function $\omega_\infty(x)$ possibly vanishes (almost) everywhere in the phase space Γ so that it does not satisfy the condition of normalization $\int_\Gamma \omega_\infty(x)\, dx = 1$. An explicit example of this possibility is given by the mechanical system with the equations of motion

$$\left.\begin{aligned}\dot{x}_1 &= x_2, \\ \dot{x}_2 &= x_1,\end{aligned}\right\}$$

the Hamiltonian function $\frac{1}{2}(x_1^2 - x_2^2)$ (cf. § 19.3) and the initial probability density

$$\overset{0}{w}(x_1, x_2) = \frac{1}{2\pi}\exp\left[-(x_1^2 + x_2^2)\right].$$

Then

$$\begin{aligned}w(x_1, x_2, t) &= \frac{1}{2\pi}\exp\left\{-(x_1\cosh t - x_2\sinh t)^2\right. \\ &\qquad \left. -(x_1\sinh t - x_2\cosh t)^2\right\} \\ &= \frac{1}{2\pi}\exp\left\{-\tfrac{1}{2}(x_1 - x_2)^2\,\mathrm{e}^{2t} - \tfrac{1}{2}(x_1 + x_2)^2\,\mathrm{e}^{-2t}\right\}.\end{aligned}$$

Hence
$$\omega(x_1, x_2) = \lim_{t\to\infty} w(x_1, x_2, t) = \begin{cases} 1/2\pi & \text{if} \quad x_1 = x_2, \\ 0 & \text{if} \quad x_1 \neq x_2, \end{cases}$$

and
$$\int_\Gamma \omega_\infty(x)\,\mathrm{d}x = 0.$$

19.7. THEOREM. *If, under the assumptions of Theorem* 19.6, *there is an invariant subset J of positive finite measure such that its initial probability*

$$\int_J \overset{0}{w}(x)\,\mathrm{d}x = 1,$$

then the non-negative invariant function $\omega_\infty(x)$ *satisfies the condition of normalization, namely*

$$\int_J \omega_\infty(x)\,\mathrm{d}x = 1.$$

In other words, under the assumptions given above, the time average $\omega(x, t)$ of the probability density $w(x, t)$ tends towards a time-independent probability density $\omega_\infty(x)$, as $t \to \infty$. One may expect that the mechanical system will at last reach statistical equilibrium in this sense after a period which is very much larger than its time scale.

Proof. From

$$\int_J \omega(x, t)\,\mathrm{d}x = 1$$

(by Theorem 19.6), it follows that

$$\left(1 - \int_J \omega_\infty \, dx\right)^2 = \left\{\int_J \omega(x,t)\,dx - \int_J \omega_\infty(x)\,dx\right\}^2$$

$$= \left\{\int_J (\omega - \omega_\infty)\,dx\right\}^2$$

$$\leqslant \int_J (\omega - \omega_\infty)^2\,dx \cdot \int_J dx$$

(by Schwarz' inequality 9.2). The theorem is now obtained by letting $t \to \infty$.

Note. According to Birkhoff's Theorem 13.5, $\omega(x,t)$ converges, under the assumptions of the theorem, towards $\omega_\infty(x)$ at almost all points x of J, and not only "in the mean" (as under the assumptions of § 19.6).

CoROLLARY. *Let J be an invariant subset of the phase space Γ of finite measure such that there is no invariant subset of $\Gamma - J$ of finite positive measure. Then*

$$\begin{cases} \int_J \omega_\infty(x)\,dx = \int_J \overset{0}{w}(x)\,dx, \\ \int_{\Gamma-J} \omega_\infty(x)\,dx = 0 \end{cases}$$

and, therefore, $\quad 0 \leqslant \int_\Gamma \omega_\infty(x)\,dx = \int_J \overset{0}{w}(x)\,dx \leqslant 1.$

The initial probability density $\overset{0}{w}(x)$ can always be chosen in such a fashion that $\int_\Gamma \omega_\infty(x)\,dx$ takes any value of the closed interval $0 \ldots 1$, provided that there is an invariant set of positive finite measure. If there is none, $\int_\Gamma \omega_\infty(x)\,dx = 0$.

Hence a mechanical system does not tend towards a state of statistical equilibrium if either such a state is not possible at all (because there is no suitable invariant set), or if the initial probability has an unsuitable distribution, such that

$$\int_J \overset{0}{w}(x)\,dx < 1.$$

The *proof* of the first equation of the corollary is similar to that of Theorem 19.7, and the proof of the second equation is similar to that of Theorem 19.3. For the latter, denote by J_λ the set of all the points of x of $\Gamma - J$ for which $\lambda \leqslant \omega_\infty(x) < \lambda + 1$ where $\lambda = 1, 2, \ldots$, and denote by i_λ the set of all the points x of $\Gamma - J$ for which

$$\frac{1}{\lambda} > \omega_\infty(x) \geqslant \frac{1}{\lambda + 1}.$$

All these sets are measurable and invariant. From

$$\int_{\Gamma - J} \omega_\infty^2 \, dx = \sum_{\lambda=1}^{\infty} \int_{J_\lambda} \omega_\infty^2 \, dx + \sum_{\lambda=1}^{\infty} \int_{i_\lambda} \omega_\infty^2 \, dx$$

it follows that

$$\sum_{\lambda=1}^{\infty} \left\{ \lambda^2 \cdot \mu J_\lambda + \frac{\mu i_\lambda}{(\lambda + 1)^2} \right\} \leqslant \int_{\Gamma - J} \omega_\infty^2 \, dx$$
$$\leqslant \sum_{\lambda=1}^{\infty} \left\{ (\lambda + 1)^2 \mu J_\lambda + \frac{\mu i_\lambda}{\lambda^2} \right\}.$$

Hence all the values of μJ_λ and μi_λ are finite. Now suppose that, in contradiction to the second equation, $\int_{\Gamma - J} \omega_\infty^2 \, dx > 0$. Then at least one of the values $\mu J_\lambda, \mu i_\lambda$ is positive. But this contradicts the assumption that $\Gamma - J$ does not contain an invariant subset of positive finite measure. Hence all the values of $\mu J_\lambda, \mu i_\lambda$ vanish, and so does $\int_{\Gamma - J} \omega_\infty(x) \, dx$. The rest of the corollary is evident.

References

A summarizing report about the theory of liquids is given by

[35] COLE, G. H. A., Theory of Monatomic Liquids at Ordinary Temperatures, *Reports on Progress in Physics*, XIX, 1956.

For the theory of functional equations in general spaces, cf.

[36] HILLE, E., *Functional Analysis and Semi-groups* (American Mathematical Society, 1948).

The fundamental equations of hydromechanics were derived in a different way and in a somewhat different form by

[37] NOLL, W., Die Herleitung der Grundgleichungen der Thermomechanik der Kontinua aus der statistischen Mechanik, *J. Rat. Mech. Anal.*, **4**, 627–646, 1955.

120   AXIOMATICS OF STATISTICAL MECHANICS

For the initial value problem, cf.

[38] MORGENSTERN, D., Analytical Studies related to the Maxwell–
Boltzmann Equation, *J. Rat. Mech. Anal.*, **4**, 533, 1955.

[39] KURTH, R., Das Anfangswertproblem der Stellardynamik,
Z. Astrophys., **30**, 213, 1952.

[40] KURTH, R., Das Anfangswertproblem der statistischen
Mechanik, *J. Math. Mech.*, **7**, 29, 1958.

For certain special cases, Morgenstern proves the tendency of
mechanical systems towards statistical equilibrium, under the assumption that Boltzmann's (or a very similar) equation is valid. For its
physical derivation and discussion, see, for example, Boltzmann's book
[24] or the very readable account by

[41] ROCARD, Y., *L'hydrodynamique et la théorie cinétique des gaz*,
Paris, 1932.

Another presentation of its mathematical theory is given by

[42] CARLEMAN, T., *Problèmes mathématiques dans la théorie
cinétique des gaz*, Uppsala, 1957.

A report of Hilbert's work on this theory is found, for example, in
the book

[43] SCHMEIDLER, W., *Integralgleichungen mit Anwendungen in
Physik und Technik.*, Vol. I, Leipzig, 1950.

CHAPTER VI

TIME-INDEPENDENT
PROBABILITY DISTRIBUTIONS

§ 20. Fluctuations in statistical equilibrium

In § 19, necessary and sufficient conditions were given for the existence of statistically stationary states and for the approach (in a sense) of mechanical systems towards these states. The discrepancy between Poincaré's Recurrence Theorem and observations like the apparently irreversible passage of a gas into a vacuum (§ 12.2) has not yet, however, been completely removed: it has still to be shown that recurrence is a very rare event. This will be attempted now.

20.1. TSCHEBYSCHEFF'S INEQUALITY. *Let $\mathring{w}(x)$ be the initial probability density of a mechanical system in its phase space Γ, and $g(x)$ be a non-negative function which is measurable in Γ and for which there is a "phase average" $\bar{g}$ defined by*

$$\bar{g} = \int_\Gamma g(x)\,\mathring{w}(x)\,\mathrm{d}x.$$

Then the probability of the set $[g(x) \geqslant \epsilon]$ of all the points x of Γ for which $g(x) \geqslant \epsilon$, where ϵ is any positive constant, is given by

$$\mathring{P}[g(x) \geqslant \epsilon] \leqslant \frac{\bar{g}}{\epsilon}.$$

Proof.
$$\mathring{P}[g(x) \geqslant \epsilon] = \int_{[g(x) \geqslant \epsilon]} \mathring{w}(x)\,\mathrm{d}x$$

$$= \frac{1}{\epsilon} \int_{[g(x) \geqslant \epsilon]} \epsilon\,\mathring{w}(x)\,\mathrm{d}x$$

$$\leqslant \frac{1}{\epsilon} \int_{[g(x) \geqslant \epsilon]} g(x)\,\mathring{w}(x)\,\mathrm{d}x$$

$$\leqslant \frac{1}{\epsilon} \int_\Gamma g(x)\,\mathring{w}(x)\,\mathrm{d}x.$$

Q.E.D.

20.2. Theorem. *Let $w(x)$ be a time-independent probability density of a mechanical system with a stationary measure-conserving phase flow χ. Further, let $g(x)$ be a phase function for which phase averages*

$$\bar{g} = \int_\Gamma g(x)\,w(x)\,\mathrm{d}x \quad and \quad \overline{g^2} = \int_\Gamma \{g(x)\}^2\,w(x)\,\mathrm{d}x$$

exist. Then, at any instant t, the phase average $\bar{\hat{g}}$ of the time average $\hat{g}(\overset{\scriptscriptstyle 0}{x}, t)$ exists and is equal to the phase average of the function $g(x)$ itself, and the "variance" $\overline{(\hat{g}-\bar{\hat{g}})^2}$ of the time average exists and is not larger than the variance $\overline{(g-\bar{g})^2}$ of $g(x)$.

Proof.
$$\bar{\hat{g}} = \int_\Gamma \frac{1}{t}\int_0^t g\{\chi(\overset{\scriptscriptstyle 0}{x},\tau)\}\,\mathrm{d}\tau\, w(\overset{\scriptscriptstyle 0}{x})\,\mathrm{d}\overset{\scriptscriptstyle 0}{x}$$

$$= \frac{1}{t}\int_0^t\int_\Gamma g\{\chi(\overset{\scriptscriptstyle 0}{x},\tau)\}\,w(\overset{\scriptscriptstyle 0}{x})\,\mathrm{d}\overset{\scriptscriptstyle 0}{x}\,\mathrm{d}\tau$$
$$\text{(§§ 8.15 and 13.2)}$$

$$= \frac{1}{t}\int_0^t\int_\Gamma g(x)\,w(x)\,\mathrm{d}x\,\mathrm{d}t \qquad \text{(§ 11.5)}$$

$$= \int_\Gamma g(x)\,w(x)\,\mathrm{d}x.$$

Further,
$$\overline{(\hat{g}-\bar{\hat{g}})} = \overline{\hat{g}^2} - 2\bar{\hat{g}}\hat{g} + \hat{g}^2 = \overline{\hat{g}^2} - \bar{g}^2.$$

Now, Schwarz' inequality holds for time averages also. Hence

$$\hat{g}^2 = \widehat{1.g^2} \leqslant \widehat{1^2}\,\widehat{g^2} = \widehat{g^2},$$

$$\overline{\hat{g}^2} \qquad \leqslant \quad \overline{\widehat{g^2}} = \overline{g^2},$$

$$\overline{(\hat{g}-\bar{\hat{g}})^2} = \overline{\hat{g}^2} - \bar{g}^2 \leqslant \overline{g^2} - \bar{g}^2 = \overline{(g-\bar{g})^2}.$$

$$\text{Q.E.D.}$$

Corollary I. *Let L be a Lebesgue subset of Γ and $\delta_L(x)$ its characteristic function. Then, at any moment t, the expectation value $\bar{\hat{\delta}}_L$ of the relative period (relativ Verweilzeit) $\hat{\delta}_L(\overset{\scriptscriptstyle 0}{x}, t)$ of the moving phase point $\chi(\overset{\scriptscriptstyle 0}{x},t)$ in L equals the probability δ_L of L, and the variance $\overline{(\hat{\delta}_L-\bar{\delta}_L)^2}$ of the relative period is not larger than $\delta_L(1-\delta_L)$.*

Corollary II. *There are functions $g(x)$ such that*

$$\overline{(\hat{g}-\bar{\hat{g}})^2} = \overline{(g-\bar{g})^2}.$$

Therefore, the upper bound $\overline{(g-\bar{g})^2}$ of the variance $\overline{(\hat{g}-\bar{\hat{g}})^2}$ cannot be lowered without particular assumptions about the function $g(x)$.

Example. Consider a "linear harmonic oscillator", of which the Hamiltonian function is $\frac{1}{2}(x_1^2+x_2^2)$ and the equations of motion read

$$\left.\begin{aligned}\dot{x}_1 &= -x_2, \\ \dot{x}_2 &= +x_1.\end{aligned}\right\}$$

Let J be the set of all points x such that $xx \leqslant 1$, and L be the set of all x for which $xx \leqslant \frac{1}{2}$, and $w(x) = \delta_J(x)/\mu J$. Then

$$\hat{\delta}_L(\overset{\scriptscriptstyle 0}{x}, t) = \delta_L(\overset{\scriptscriptstyle 0}{x}),$$

$$\bar{\hat{\delta}}_L = \bar{\delta}_L = \frac{\mu L}{\mu J} = \frac{1}{2},$$

$$\overline{(\hat{\delta}_L - \bar{\hat{\delta}}_L)^2} = \overline{\hat{\delta}_L^2} - \bar{\hat{\delta}}_L^2$$

$$= \overline{\delta_L^2} - \bar{\delta}_L^2$$

$$= \overline{(\delta_L - \bar{\delta}_L)^2}.$$

20.3. THEOREM. *Suppose that, under the assumptions of Theorem 20.2, $\bar{g} > 0$. Then, for any positive constant ϵ and at any instant t*

$$\left.\begin{aligned}P[|\hat{g}-\bar{\hat{g}}| \geqslant \epsilon\bar{\hat{g}}]\\ P[|g-\bar{g}| \geqslant \epsilon\bar{g}]\end{aligned}\right\} \leqslant \frac{1}{\epsilon^2}\frac{\overline{(g-\bar{g})^2}}{\bar{g}^2},$$

where $P[...]$ denotes the probability of the set of all those points of Γ which satisfy the relation written in the square brackets.

Proof.

$$P[|\hat{g}-\bar{\hat{g}}| \geqslant \epsilon\bar{\hat{g}}] = P[(\hat{g}-\bar{\hat{g}})^2 \geqslant \epsilon^2\bar{\hat{g}}^2], \text{ etc.}$$

Now apply Theorems 20.1 and 20.2.

20.4. A function $g(x)$ for which the right-hand side of the inequalities 20.3 is small even if ϵ is small is, very probably, approximately "ergodic" (cf. § 13.6) and approximately constant. An important class of such functions will now be considered.

DEFINITIONS. Let $x^1, x^2, ..., x^k$ be components of the phase vector x of a mechanical system such that $x = (x^1, x^2, ..., x^k)$.

(Cf. § 16.3.) Then a phase function $g(x)$ having the form

$$g(x) \equiv \sum_{\kappa=1}^{k} f^{\kappa}(x^{\kappa})$$

is said to be a *sum function*. Two components x^1 and x^2 are called *equivalent* if $w(x^1, x^2, x^3, \ldots, x^n, t) \equiv w(x^2, x^1, x^3, \ldots, x^n, t)$. (Cf. Definition 17.5.) If all the components of a system are equivalent, a phase function $g(x)$ of the form

$$g(x) \equiv \sum_{\kappa=1}^{k} f(x^{\kappa})$$

is named a *special sum function*.

Notes. There are theorems about equivalent components which are generalizations of Theorems 17.5 and 17.6 about equivalent mass-points.

Many observable quantities can be represented by means of sum functions. Consider, for example, a system of n mass-points. Let B' be any Borel subset of the 6-dimensional position-momentum space Γ', and B^{ν}, $\nu = 1, 2, \ldots, n$, be its congruent images in the phase spaces Γ^{ν} of the single particles. Then the number of all the mass-points in B' is given by the sum function

$$N \equiv \sum_{\nu=1}^{n} \delta_{B^{\nu}}(x^{\nu}) \equiv \sum_{\nu=1}^{n} \delta_{B^{\nu} \times (\Gamma/\Gamma^{\nu})}(x)$$

where the symbol δ denotes characteristic functions.

The following propositions are given purely for the sake of simpler formulation for special sum functions only. They can be generalized to any sum functions without difficulty.

20.5. THEOREM. *Let a mechanical system have a stationary measure-conserving phase flow χ and a time-independent probability density $w(x)$. Assume that the phase vector x consists of k equivalent components $x^1, x^2, \ldots, x^k$, and that both the function $f(x^1)$ and its square $\{f(x^1)\}^2$ possess positive phase averages $\bar{f}$ and $\overline{f^2}$. Put $g(x) \equiv \sum_{\kappa=1}^{k} f(x^{\kappa})$, let ϵ be a positive constant, and γ be the "correlation coefficient" of the functions $f^1 \equiv f(x^1)$ and $f^2 \equiv f(x^2)$, defined by*

$$\gamma = \frac{\overline{(f^1 - \bar{f})(f^2 - \bar{f})}}{\overline{(f - \bar{f})^2}}.$$

Then, at any instant t,

$$\left.\begin{array}{l} P[|\hat{g}-\bar{g}| \geqslant \epsilon\bar{g}] \\ P[|g-\bar{g}| \geqslant \epsilon\bar{g}] \end{array}\right\} \leqslant \frac{1}{\epsilon^2} \frac{\overline{(f-\bar{f})^2}}{\bar{f}^2} \left\{\frac{1}{k}+\max(0,\gamma)\right\}.$$

Proof.
$$\bar{g} = k\bar{f},$$

$$\overline{(g-\bar{g})^2} = k\overline{(f-\bar{f})^2} + k(k-1)\,\overline{(f^1-\bar{f})(f^2-\bar{f})}$$
$$= \{k+k(k-1)\,\gamma\}\,\overline{(f-\bar{f})^2}.$$

Now apply Theorem 20.3.

COROLLARY. *Let Γ' be a phase space corresponding to a single component of the system, L' be a Lebesgue subset of Γ', L^κ, $\kappa = 1,...,k$, be the congruent image of L' in the phase space Γ^κ of the κth component, and ϵ be any positive constant. Assume that the cylindric sets $C^\kappa = L^\kappa \times (\Gamma/\Gamma^\kappa)$ erected over L^κ in Γ possess a positive probability δ_{C^1}. Then the following relations hold for the number N of all components in L'*

$$\bar{N} = k\delta_{C^1},$$

$$\left.\begin{array}{l} P[|\hat{N}-\bar{N}| \geqslant \epsilon\bar{N}] \\ P[|N-\bar{N}| > \epsilon\bar{N}] \end{array}\right\} \leqslant \frac{1}{\epsilon^2} \frac{1-\delta_{C^1}}{\delta_{C^1}} \left\{\frac{1}{k}+\max(0,\gamma)\right\}$$

where γ denotes the correlation coefficient of the functions $\delta_{L^1}(x^1)$ and $\delta_{L^2}(x^2)$.

Notes. On account of the equations

$$\left.\begin{array}{l} \hat{N} = k\delta_{C^1}, \\ \bar{N} = k\delta_{C^1}, \end{array}\right\}$$

the inequality for $P[|\hat{N}-\bar{N}| \geqslant \epsilon\bar{N}]$ can be interpreted as a proposition about the deviation of the relative period (*Verweilzeit*) δ_{C^1} of the moving phase point in the set C^1 from the probability of this set:

$$\bar{\delta}_{C^1} = \delta_{C^1},$$

$$P[|\delta_{C^1}-\delta_{C^1}| \geqslant \epsilon\delta_{C^1}] \leqslant \frac{1}{\epsilon^2} \frac{1-\delta_{C^1}}{\delta_{C^1}} \left\{\frac{1}{k}+\max(0,\gamma)\right\}\Bigg\}.$$

δ_{C^1} can also be understood as the relative period of the 1st component x^1 in the set L^1.

Finally, the corollary can be interpreted as a proposition about the relation between the fractional number N/k of components in L' and the probability of this set.

The last interpretation is an analogy of the "law of large numbers" in general statistics. Suppose an event E has the probability p and its "complement" F (i.e. the event that E does not take place) the probability $q = 1 - p$. Now define a "space" Γ' which consists only of the two "points" E and F; define, further, k congruent spaces $\Gamma^\kappa = \{E^\kappa, F^\kappa\}$, $\kappa = 1, 2, \ldots, k$, with the probability distributions $P^\kappa(E^\kappa) = p$, $P^\kappa(F^\kappa) = q$, and define, finally, a space $\Gamma = \Gamma^1 \times \Gamma^2 \times \ldots \times \Gamma^k$ with the probability distribution

$$P(x^1, x^2, \ldots, x^k) \equiv P^1(x^1) P^2(x^2) \ldots P^k(x^k).$$

Let $\delta_{E^\kappa}(x^\kappa)$ be the characteristic function of the set E^κ in Γ^κ. Then the sum function

$$N = \sum_{\kappa=1}^{k} \delta_{E^\kappa}(x^\kappa)$$

yields the number of "components" in the subset E of Γ' for a given "phase point" $x = (x^1, \ldots, x^k)$, i.e. the number of times that E happens for a given x. Thus,

$$\left. \begin{aligned} \bar{N} &= kp, \\ \overline{(N - \bar{N})^2} &= kp(1 - p) \end{aligned} \right\}$$

and

$$P\left[\left| \frac{N}{k} - p \right| \geqslant \epsilon p \right] \leqslant \frac{1}{\epsilon^2} \frac{1 - p}{p} \frac{1}{k}$$

—well-known formulae, which are usually derived by means of the binomial theorem.

20.6. The fertility of Theorem 20.5 depends on how small the correlation coefficient γ is. One is inclined to expect that, for a large number k of components, $|\gamma|$ is small. This, however, is not necessarily true, as is shown by the example of the rigid body, i.e. a system of particles whose mutual distances are (nearly) constant. For a special case, the supposition will now be demonstrated, and a more general case will be dealt with in § 21.

THEOREM. *Assume that the sphere J defined by the inequality $|x| \leqslant \sigma \sqrt{(n+2)}$ is an invariant subset of the n-dimensional phase* *space* Γ. *Here σ denotes a positive constant. Let $\delta_J(x)/\mu J$ be the probability density in Γ. Then the probability density $w^1(x^1)$ of the l-dimensional component x^1 is given by*

$$w^1(x^1) = \begin{cases} (2\pi\sigma)^{-l/2}\exp\left(-x^1 x^1/2\sigma^2\right)[1+o(1)] \\ \qquad \text{if} \quad |x^1| \leqslant \sigma\sqrt{(n+2)} \quad \text{and} \quad n\to\infty, \\ 0 \qquad \text{if} \quad |x^1| > \sigma\sqrt{(n+2)}. \end{cases}$$

For each value of n, the variance $\overline{x_\nu x_\nu}$ of any one-dimensional component x_ν, $\nu = 1, \ldots, n$, of the phase vector x equals σ^2.

Proof. For $|x^1| \leqslant \sigma\sqrt{(n+2)}$, the probability density $w^1(x^1)$ is proportional to the volume of the $(n-1)$-dimensional sphere with the radius $\sqrt{[(n+2)\sigma^2 - x^1 x^1]}$ (see the figure) and, therefore, to $\{(n+2)\sigma^2 - x^1 x^1\}^{\frac{1}{2}(n-l)}$ or $[1 - \{x^1 x^1/(n+2)\sigma^2\}]^{\frac{1}{2}(n-l)}$. For $n\to\infty$, this expression tends towards $e^{-x^1 x^1/2\sigma^2}$. Further, for each value of n,

$$\overline{xx} = \frac{\displaystyle\int_0^{\sigma\sqrt{(n+2)}} r^2 . r^{n-1}\,\mathrm{d}r}{\displaystyle\int_0^{\sigma\sqrt{(n+2)}} r^{n-1}\,\mathrm{d}r} = n\sigma^2.$$

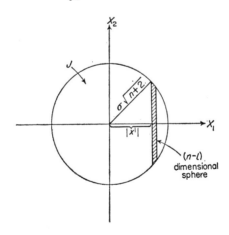

On the other hand,

$$\overline{xx} = \sum_{\nu=1}^{n} \overline{x_\nu x_\nu} = n\,\overline{x_1 x_1}.$$

Hence

$$\overline{x_1 x_1} = \sigma^2. \qquad\qquad \text{Q.E.D.}$$

COROLLARY. For sufficiently large values of n the correlation coefficient of any two (integrable) functions $f(x^1)$ and $f(x^2)$ is arbitrarily small.

20.7. The following analogue of Theorem 20.5 deals once more with the approach of mechanical systems towards macroscopically stationary states.

THEOREM. *Let J be an invariant subset of the phase space Γ of finite measure, $\overset{\circ}{x}$ be any initial point in J, $g(x) \equiv \sum\limits_{\kappa=1}^{k} f^\kappa(x^\kappa)$ be a sum function whose terms are integrable over J and satisfy the conditions*

$$0 < m \leqslant f^\kappa(x^\kappa) \leqslant M, \quad \kappa = 1, 2, \ldots, k, \quad m = \text{const.}, \quad M = \text{const.},$$

ϵ be a positive constant, $G(\overset{\circ}{x}, t^*)$ the set of all the instants t of the interval $0 \leqslant t \leqslant t^*$ for which $|g(\overset{\circ}{x}, t) - \hat{g}(\overset{\circ}{x}, t)| \geqslant \epsilon \hat{g}(\overset{\circ}{x}, t)$, the initial point $\overset{\circ}{x}$ being fixed. Then, for any instant $t^* > 0$ and almost all initial points $\overset{\circ}{x}$ of J, the set $G(\overset{\circ}{x}, t^*)$ possesses a one-dimensional measure $\tau G(\overset{\circ}{x}, t^*)$. If β denotes the largest of the correlation coefficients

$$\beta_{\kappa\lambda} \equiv \frac{[(f^\kappa - \hat{f}^\kappa)(f^\lambda - \hat{f}^\lambda)]^\wedge}{\sqrt{[(f^\kappa - \hat{f}^\kappa)^2]^\wedge}\sqrt{[(f^\lambda - \hat{f}^\lambda)^2]^\wedge}}$$

computed by means of the probability density

$$\left. \begin{array}{lll} 1/t^* & \text{if} & 0 \leqslant t \leqslant t^*, \\ 0 & \text{if} & t < 0 \quad \text{or} \quad t > t^* \end{array} \right\}$$

on the time axis, then

$$\frac{\tau G(\overset{\circ}{x}, t^*)}{t^*} \leqslant \frac{1}{\epsilon^2}\left(\frac{M}{m} - 1\right)\left(\frac{1}{k} + \beta\right)$$

for almost all $\overset{\circ}{x}$ of J. If $t^* \to \infty$, β tends towards a certain limit, which depends on $\overset{\circ}{x}$, for almost all points $\overset{\circ}{x}$ of J.

Proof. By Theorems 13.2 and 8.4, the sets $G(\overset{\circ}{x}, t^*)$ are measurable for almost all points $\overset{\circ}{x}$ of J. The proof of the inequality for $\tau G(\overset{\circ}{x}, t^*)$ is similar to that of Theorem 20.5. The existence of the limit of β follows from Birkhoff's Second Theorem 13.5.

Note. The significance of the theorem is based on the expectation (which appears plausible) that, for large values of k and t^*, the quantity β will be very small, i.e. that during a long interval of time the motions of any two components will be nearly independent of each other, if the number of components is large. If this supposition is correct, the theorem can be used to pursue the approach of the system towards its final stage. Since $\lim_{t^* \to 0} \beta_{\kappa\lambda} = 1$, the quantity β will in course of time decrease from the initial value 1 towards a small value. A considerable change of β probably needs at least a period of the order of the time scale T. (Cf. § 19.1.)

A strict proof of these suppositions, however, appears extremely difficult and is, in any case, not yet available. The use of the phase correlation coefficient γ, introduced in Theorem 20.5, is much simpler. Its value will be estimated in the next section.

§ 21. Gibbs's canonic probability distribution

In this section, mechanical systems will be considered which are described by time-independent Hamiltonian equations of motion. By Theorem 10.5, the Hamiltonian function $H(x)$ is a time-independent First Integral of them. Each function of $H(x)$ alone is also a time-independent First Integral. The subject of this section is time-independent probability densities $w(x)$ which can be represented as functions $W\{H(x)\}$ of the value of the Hamiltonian function only.

21.1. *Plausible argument.* Assume that the Hamiltonian function $H(x)$ of a mechanical system has the special form

$$H(x) \equiv \sum_{\kappa=1}^{k} H^\kappa(x^\kappa) + R(x)$$

where $x^1, \ldots, x^k$ are components of the phase vector x, $k \gg 1$, and $R(x)$ is an "interaction term" which, "in general", is "very small". Say, in order to fix our ideas: $0 \leqslant \bar{R} \ll \bar{H}$. If this interaction term is neglected completely, then, for the component x^1,

$$w^1(x^1) = \int_{\Gamma/\Gamma^1} w(x)\, \mathrm{d}(x/x^1)$$
$$= \int_{\Gamma/\Gamma^1} W\{H(x)\}\, \mathrm{d}(x/x^1)$$
$$= W^1\{H^1(x^1)\};$$

similarly, for the second component,

$$w^2(x^2) = W^2\{H^2(x^2)\};$$

and for the combined component (x^1, x^2),

$$w^{12}(x^1, x^2) = W^{12}\{H^1(x^1) + H^2(x^2)\}.$$

Now assume, because of the smallness of the interaction between the components x^1 and x^2, that

$$w^{12}(x^1, x^2) = w^1(x^1) w^2(x^2).$$

Hence $$W^1(H^1) W^2(H^2) = W^{12}(H^1 + H^2).$$

Under the assumption that all the functions are differentiable, it follows from the last equation by logarithmic differentiation with respect to H^1 that

$$\frac{1}{W^1}\frac{dW^1}{dH^1} = \frac{1}{W^{12}}\frac{dW^{12}}{d(H^1 + H^2)};$$

further, by logarithmic differentiation with respect to H^2,

$$\frac{1}{W^2}\frac{dW^2}{dH^2} = \frac{1}{W^{12}}\frac{dW^{12}}{d(H^1 + H^2)};$$

and, finally, by equating left-hand sides of the last two equations,

$$\frac{1}{W^1}\frac{dW^1}{dH^1} = \frac{1}{W^2}\frac{dW^2}{dH^2}$$

for all (admitted) values of H^1 and H^2. Therefore,

$$\frac{1}{W^1}\frac{dW^1}{dH^1} = -\vartheta \text{ const.} < 0,$$

and $$w^1(x^1) = \text{const.} \exp[-\vartheta H^1(x^1)].$$

This is *Boltzmann's probability density* for the component x^1 or *"Boltzmann's Law"*.

Notes. The constant ϑ must be assumed positive since otherwise the condition of normalization

$$\int_{\Gamma^1} w^1(x^1) dx^1 = 1$$

would not be fulfilled.

Boltzmann's Law would also have been obtained if, for the probability density $w(x)$ in Γ, the *"canonical probability density"* had been assumed, which is given by

$$w(x) \equiv \text{const.} \exp\left[-\vartheta H(x)\right],$$

and was introduced by Gibbs. If, for the moment, Boltzmann's Law is accepted as already demonstrated, the relation with the canonic probability density, apparently trivial, is in fact rather curious. If we assume that $H(x) \geqslant H(0) = 0$ (cf. Corollary 19.4), then the canonic density takes, for the energy value zero, a particularly large value. The true value of the energy of the system, however, is certainly not zero, for then the system would be at rest. Nevertheless, Gibbs's obviously incorrect expression yields a correct (and essential) consequence, namely, Boltzmann's Law. The rigorous derivation of Boltzmann's probability density, in § 21.4, will explain this observation.

If the probability density $w(x)$ in Γ depends on the Energy Integral $H(x)$ and any other First Integral $K(x)$ which is a sum function, too, so that

$$K(x) = \sum_{\kappa=1}^{k} K^\nu(x^\nu),$$

then a similar argument leads to the following generalization of Boltzmann's Law:

$$w^1(x^1) = \text{const.} \exp\left[-\vartheta H^1(x^1) - \eta K^1(x^1)\right],$$

where ϑ and η are constants. Such integrals are, for example, those of linear and angular momentum (§ 10.6). The direct calculation shows that, to a component of the angular momentum taken as function $K(x)$, there corresponds a rigid rotation of the system around the axis concerned, with angular velocity η/ϑ.

21.2. LEMMA (APPROXIMATION THEOREM OF WEIERSTRASS). *Let $f(x)$ be a (scalar) continuous function of the real variable x defined in the closed bounded one-dimensional interval i. Then, for any positive constant η, there is a polynomial $Q(x)$ of x such that $|Q(x) - f(x)| < \eta$ for each x of i.*

Proof. By Theorem 5.2, $f(x)$ is uniformly continuous in i, i.e.

$$|f(x_b) - f(x_a)| \leqslant \epsilon \quad \text{if} \quad |x_b - x_a| \leqslant \delta, \quad x_a \in i, \, x_b \in i.$$

Hence, by a suitable subdivision of the interval $x \ldots x'$, where x and x' are any two points of i, by numbers $x_1, x_2, \ldots, x_r$, it follows that

$$|f(x')-f(x)| \leqslant |f(x_1)-f(x)| + |f(x_2)-f(x_1)| + \ldots +$$
$$+ |f(x')-f(x_r)| \leqslant \epsilon\left(\frac{|x'-x|}{\delta}+1\right). \qquad (*)$$

Now define a continuous function $f^*(x)$ on the whole x-axis such that in i it coincides with $f(x)$, that the inequality (*) holds for all values of x and x', and that $f^*(x)$ differs from zero only in a bounded interval of the x-axis. Further, define a function $g(x)$ on the x-axis by

$$g(x) = \int_{-\infty}^{+\infty} f^*(y)\frac{\exp\left[-(x-y)^2/\sigma^2\right]}{\sigma\sqrt{\pi}}\,dy$$

where σ denotes a positive constant. Then, for all values of x,

$$|g(x)-f^*(x)| \leqslant \int_{-\infty}^{+\infty}|f^*(y)-f^*(x)|\frac{\exp\left[-(x-y)^2/\sigma^2\right]}{\sigma\sqrt{\pi}}\,dy$$
$$\leqslant \int_{-\infty}^{+\infty}\epsilon\left(1+\frac{|y-x|}{\delta}\right)\frac{\exp\left[-(x-y)/\sigma^2\right]}{\sigma\sqrt{\pi}}\,dy$$
$$= \epsilon\left(1+\frac{1}{\sqrt{\pi}}\frac{\sigma}{\delta}\right).$$

For suitable values of ϵ, δ, σ (to be chosen in this order), the right-hand side becomes smaller than $\frac{1}{2}\eta$. Now the function $\exp\left[-(x-y)^2/\sigma^2\right]$ and, therefore, the function $g(x)$ can be expanded into a power series with respect to x, which converges for all values of x, and converges uniformly in the interval i. So it can be uniformly approximated in i by the polynomial $Q(x)$ which consists of a sufficiently long section of the first terms of the series. Thus,

$$|Q(x)-g(x)| \leqslant \tfrac{1}{2}\eta,$$

for a suitable polynomial $Q(x)$, and

$$|Q(x)-f(x)| \leqslant |Q(x)-g(x)| + |g(x)-f^*(x)| \quad (\text{if } x \in i)$$
$$< \eta. \qquad\qquad \text{Q.E.D.}$$

21.3. THEOREM. *Suppose that, for a mechanical system governed by a time-independent Hamiltonian function $H(x)$,*

$$H(x) \geqslant H(0) = 0,$$
$$H(x) \to \infty \quad \text{if} \quad |x| \to \infty,$$

that the probability density $w(x)$ is a continuous function of the value of the Hamiltonian function only and that

$$\lim_{|x| \to \infty} w(x)$$

exists. Then, for any two positive constants ϑ and η, there is a polynomial

$$Q(u) = \sum_{\lambda=1}^{l} a_\lambda u^\lambda$$

of the (scalar) variable u such that

$$|Q\{\exp[-\vartheta H(x)]\} - w(x)| < \eta$$

at all points x of the phase space Γ.

This is an immediate application of the Weierstrass Approximation Theorem 21.2.

Note. Let $g(x)$ be any function which is integrable over Γ. Then, by Theorem 8.5, the functions $g(x)Q\{\exp[-\vartheta H(x)]\}$ and $g(x)w(x)$ are integrable over Γ, as well. ($w(x)$ is bounded.) The theorem now yields the following relation between their integrals

$$\left| \int_\Gamma Q\{\exp[-\vartheta H(x)]\} g(x) \, \mathrm{d}x - \bar{g} \right| \leqslant \eta \int_\Gamma |g(x)| \, \mathrm{d}x.$$

Therefore, for sufficiently small values of η, the probability density $w(x)$ can be replaced, in the calculation of the phase average g, by the "polynomial" $Q\{\exp[-\vartheta H(x)]\}$, the error being arbitrarily small. Hence, for practical purposes, we are now entitled to suppose that the probability density can be represented (and not only approximated) by a polynomial

$$\sum_{\lambda=1}^{l} a_\lambda \exp[-\lambda \vartheta H(x)].$$

The assumption that $w(x)$ is continuous is not actually essential, as will now be shown for the case (which is the most important in practice) of a piecewise constant probability density. Let J be the set of all the points x of Γ for which $\alpha \leqslant H(x) \leqslant \beta$ (where α and β are two suitable constants). Further, let

$$w(x) = \frac{\delta_J(x)}{J},$$

and ϵ be a positive constant. Approximate $w(x)$ by a new probability density $w^*(x)$ which depends on H continuously, by, for example,

$$w^*(x) = \text{const.} \times \begin{cases} 0 & \text{if } H(x) \leqslant \alpha - \epsilon, \\[2mm] \dfrac{H(x) - (\alpha - \epsilon)}{\epsilon} & \text{if } \alpha - \epsilon \leqslant H(x) \leqslant \alpha, \\[2mm] 1 & \text{if } \alpha \leqslant H(x) \leqslant \beta, \\[2mm] \dfrac{(\beta + \epsilon) - H(x)}{\epsilon} & \text{if } \beta \leqslant H(x) \leqslant \beta + \epsilon, \\[2mm] 0 & \text{if } \beta + \epsilon \leqslant H(x). \end{cases}$$

The constant factor has to be chosen such that the condition of normalization,

$$\int_\Gamma w^*(x)\,\mathrm{d}x = 1,$$

is fulfilled. $w^*(x)$ can be approximated by a polynomial $Q\{\exp[-\vartheta H(x)]\}$. Since for sufficiently small values of ϵ the difference

$$\left| \int_\Gamma g(x)\, w^*(x)\,\mathrm{d}x - \int_\Gamma g(x)\, w(x)\,\mathrm{d}x \right|$$

is arbitrarily small, so is the difference

$$\left| \int_\Gamma g(x)\, Q\{\exp[-\vartheta H(x)]\}\,\mathrm{d}x - \int_\Gamma g(x)\, w(x)\,\mathrm{d}x \right|$$

for a sufficiently small difference $|Q - w^*|$ and a sufficiently small value of ϵ. In the case of a more general probability density $w(x)$, the Approximation Theorem 8.5 may be applied.

21.4. THEOREM (BOLTZMANN'S LAW). *Suppose that a mechanical system consisting of k equivalent components $x^1, x^2, \ldots, x^k$ has the Hamiltonian function*

$$H(x) \equiv \sum_{\kappa=1}^{k} p^\kappa\, S(q^\kappa)\, p^\kappa + V(q).$$

Here the first terms on the right-hand side denote positive-definite quadratic forms in p^κ where p^κ is the vector of momentum of the κth component, and $S^\kappa(q^\kappa)$ is a symmetric matrix which depends only on the position vector q^κ of the κth component.

Suppose that $H(x) \geqslant H(0) = 0$, $H(x) \to \infty$ *if* $|x| \to \infty$, *and that there is a positive constant* ϑ *such that* $\exp[-\vartheta H(x)]$ *is integrable over the $2n$-dimensional phase space* Γ. *Let the probability density* $w(x)$ *of the system be given by*

$$w(x) \equiv \text{const.} \exp[-\vartheta H(x)] \left\{ 1 + \sum_{\lambda=1}^{l} a_\lambda \exp[-\lambda \vartheta H(x)] \right\}.$$

Then, for the probability density $w^1(x^1)$ *of the first component in its phase space* Γ^1,

$$w^1(x^1) = \text{const.} \exp\{-\vartheta[p^1 S(q^1) p^1 + V^*(q^1, \vartheta)]\} . [1 + \zeta(x^1)]$$

where, for any positive value of the parameter ξ, *the function* $V^*(q^1, \xi)$ *is defined by*

$$\exp[-\vartheta V^*(q^1, \xi)] \equiv \int_{\Gamma_q/\Gamma_q^1} \exp[-\xi V(q)] \prod_{\kappa=2}^{k} \{\det S^\kappa(q^\kappa)\}^{-\frac{1}{2}} . d(q/q^1),$$

and $\qquad |\zeta(x^1)| < \dfrac{\frac{1}{2}n(1-1/k)+1}{\frac{1}{2}n(1-1/k)-1} 2^{-\frac{1}{2}n(1-1/k)} . \max_{1 \leqslant \lambda \leqslant l} |a_\lambda|.$

Proof. An explicit integration of $w(x)$ over Γ/Γ^1 shows that

$$\zeta(x^1) = \sum_{\lambda=1}^{l} \frac{a_\lambda}{(\lambda+1)^{\frac{1}{2}(n/k)(k-1)}} \exp[-\vartheta p^1 . S^1(q^1) \vartheta p^1] \times$$
$$\times \frac{\exp[-\vartheta V^*(q^1, \overline{\lambda+1}\,\vartheta)]}{\exp[-\vartheta V^*(q^1, \lambda\vartheta)]}.$$

Now $\qquad \exp[-\vartheta V^*(q^1, \overline{\lambda+1}\,\vartheta)] \leqslant \exp[-\vartheta V^*(q^1, \lambda\vartheta)],$

by the definition of V^*. Hence

$$|\zeta(x^1)| \leqslant \sum_{\lambda=1}^{l} \frac{|a_\lambda|}{(\lambda+1)^{\frac{1}{2}(n/k)(k-1)}} < \max_{1 \leqslant \lambda \leqslant l} |a_\lambda| . \sum_{\lambda=2}^{\infty} \lambda^{-\frac{1}{2}(n/k)(k-1)}.$$

For $\alpha = \text{const.} > 1$,

$$\sum_{\lambda=2}^{\infty} \lambda^{-\alpha} < 2^{-\alpha} + \int_{2}^{\infty} \lambda^{-\alpha} d\lambda = 2^{-\alpha} \frac{\alpha+1}{\alpha-1}.$$

The statement of the theorem is now obtained by applying the last formula to $\alpha = \frac{1}{2}(n/k)(k-1)$.

Notes. Even for values of n and k of moderate magnitude, the factor $2^{-n(k-1)/2k}$ is already small. If, for example, the system consists of only ten mass-points, so that $k = 10$ and

$n = 30$, then

$$| \zeta^1(x^1) | < \frac{\frac{135}{10} + 1}{\frac{135}{10} - 1} 2^{-\frac{135}{10}} . \max | a_\lambda |$$

$$< 2^{-13} . \max | a_\lambda |$$

$$= \frac{1}{8192} . \max | a_\lambda |.$$

Therefore, even if the coefficients $| a_\lambda |$ are large, $\zeta(x^1)$ may, in general, be expected to be very small. Let the probability density $w(x)$ deviate from the canonic density by an arbitrarily large amount: nevertheless, for a sufficiently large number k of components, the generalized Boltzmann Law

$$w^1(x^1) = \text{const.} \exp [- \vartheta (p^1 . S^1 p^1 + V^*)]$$

will hold, *as if* $w(x)$ were Gibbs's canonic density. The "projection" of the probability density $w(x)$ down to the sub-space Γ^1 of a number of dimensions which is much smaller than the number $2n$ of dimensions of Γ, blots out most particular features of $w(x)$. When an observable quantity, which in most cases can be represented according to § 20.4 as the phase average of a sum function, is calculated by means of the canonic density (instead of the true density), a considerable error can arise only if one of the coefficients $| a_\lambda |$ is of the order $2^{n(k-1)/2k}$ at least. This fact appears as one of the major reasons why statistical mechanics is applicable at all: in many cases the probability density assumed in the phase space Γ does not matter much. There is a kind of convergence from partly subjective assumptions about the probability distribution in Γ towards considerably more objective conclusions about the probability distribution in Γ^1.

The definition of the function $V^*(q^1, \xi)$ can be written more symmetrically in the following form

$$\frac{\exp [- \vartheta V^*(q^1, \xi)]}{\{ \det S^1(q^1) \}^{\frac{1}{2}}} \equiv \int_{\Gamma/\Gamma^1} \frac{\exp [- \xi V(q)]}{\left\{ \prod_{\kappa=1}^{k} \det S^\kappa(q^\kappa) \right\}^{\frac{1}{2}}} \, \mathrm{d}(q/q^1).$$

The assumption that all the components of the system are strictly equivalent is not essential and can be relaxed.

Finally, the theorem remains essentially correct when the expression for the kinetic energy in the Hamiltonian function

$p^\kappa . S^\kappa p^\kappa$, is replaced by the more general expression

$$(p^\kappa - c^\kappa) . S^\kappa (p^\kappa - c^\kappa),$$

where the c^κ's are functions of q^κ.

21.5. The canonic probability density can be used for an estimate of the correlation coefficient γ defined in Theorem 20.5.

THEOREM. *Let* $x^1, x^2, \dots, x^k$ *be components of a mechanical system of which the Hamiltonian function reads*

$$H(x) \equiv \sum_{\kappa=1}^{k} H^\kappa(x^\kappa) + R(x).$$

Suppose that

$$\left.\begin{array}{ll} H^\kappa(x^\kappa) \geqslant H^\kappa(0) = 0, & \kappa = 1, \dots, k, \\ R(x) \ \ \geqslant R(0) \ \ = 0 & \end{array}\right\}$$

and let the probability density of the system be canonic:

$$w(x) \equiv (1/\phi) \exp[-\vartheta H(x)],$$

where ϑ *denotes a positive constant, and*

$$\phi = \int_\Gamma \exp[-\vartheta H(x)] \, dx.$$

Further, assume that the following integrals exist

$$\overline{e^{2R}} = \int_\Gamma e^{2R(x)} w(x) \, dx$$

and

$$\int_{\Gamma^1} \{f^1(x^1)\}^2 \, dx^1, \quad \int_{\Gamma^2} \{f^2(x^2)\}^2 \, dx^2,$$

$f^1(x^1)$ *and* $f^2(x^2)$ *being any two given functions which are measurable in* Γ^1, Γ^2. *Then, for the correlation coefficient*

$$\gamma^2 = \frac{\overline{(f^1 - \overline{f^1})(f^2 - \overline{f^2})}}{\{\overline{(f^1 - \overline{f^1})^2}\,\overline{(f^2 - \overline{f^2})^2}\}^{\frac{1}{2}}}$$

the asymptotic relation holds:

$$\gamma^2 = O(\vartheta^2 \overline{R^2}) \quad \text{if} \quad \vartheta^2 \overline{R^2} \to 0.$$

(Bars always denote phase averages calculated by means of the probability density $w(x)$.)

Proof. Define $\rho, \sigma, \Omega, \omega$ by

$$
\left.
\begin{aligned}
\mathrm{e}^{\vartheta\rho} &= \overline{\mathrm{e}^{\vartheta R}}, \\
\sigma^2 &= \int_{\Gamma} \{\mathrm{e}^{\vartheta(\rho-R)} - 1\}^2 \omega(x)\,\mathrm{d}x,
\end{aligned}
\right\}
$$

$$
\left.
\begin{aligned}
\omega(x) &= \frac{1}{\Omega} \exp\left[-\vartheta \sum_{\kappa=1}^{k} H^{\kappa}(x^{\kappa}) \right], \\
\Omega &= \int_{\Gamma} \exp\left[-\vartheta \sum_{1}^{k} H^{\kappa}(x^{\kappa}) \right] \mathrm{d}x.
\end{aligned}
\right\}
$$

Then,
$$
\begin{aligned}
\Omega &= \int_{\Gamma} \exp\left[-\vartheta(H-R) \right] \mathrm{d}x \\
&= \phi \cdot \frac{1}{\phi} \int_{\Gamma} \mathrm{e}^{\vartheta R}\, \mathrm{e}^{-\vartheta H}\, \mathrm{d}x. \\
&= \phi\, \mathrm{e}^{\overline{\vartheta R}} \\
&= \phi\, \mathrm{e}^{\vartheta\rho}.
\end{aligned}
$$

Hence,
$$
w(x) = \exp\left[\vartheta(\rho-R) \right] \omega(x),
$$
$$
w(x) - \omega(x) = \{\exp\left[\vartheta(\rho-R) \right] - 1\}\, \omega(x)
$$

and, for any measurable function $h(x)$ of which the square is integrable over Γ,

$$
\left| \int_{\Gamma} h(x)\, w(x)\, \mathrm{d}x - \int_{\Gamma} h(x)\, \omega(x)\, \mathrm{d}x \right|
$$

$$
\leqslant \int_{\Gamma} |h(x)| \cdot |\exp\left[\vartheta(\rho-R) \right] - 1|\, \omega(x)\, \mathrm{d}x
$$

$$
\leqslant \left\{ \int_{\Gamma} h^2\, \omega\, \mathrm{d}x \right\}^{\frac{1}{2}} \left[\int_{\Gamma} \{\exp\left[\vartheta(\rho-R) \right] - 1\}^2\, \omega\, \mathrm{d}x \right]^{\frac{1}{2}},
$$

by Schwarz' inequality 9.2. By applying this inequality to $\overline{f^1 f^2}$ and $\overline{f^1}\,\overline{f^2}$, the asymptotic relation $\gamma = O(\sigma)$, if $\sigma \to \infty$, is established. Now

$$
\begin{aligned}
\sigma^2 &= \int_{\Gamma} \{\exp\left[2\vartheta(\rho-R) \right] - 2\exp\left[\vartheta(\rho-R) \right] + 1\} \times \\
&\qquad\qquad \times \exp\left[-\vartheta(\rho-R) \right] w(x)\, \mathrm{d}x \\
&= \overline{\mathrm{e}^{\vartheta(\rho-R)}} - 2 + \overline{\mathrm{e}^{-\vartheta(\rho-R)}} \\
&= \overline{\mathrm{e}^{\vartheta R}}\,\overline{\mathrm{e}^{-\vartheta R}} - 1,
\end{aligned}
$$

by the definition of ρ. Hence, by Taylor's Theorem,

$$\sigma^2 = (1 + \vartheta \bar{R} + \tfrac{1}{2}\vartheta^2 \, \overline{R^2 \, \mathrm{e}^{\alpha \vartheta R}})(1 - \vartheta \bar{R} + \tfrac{1}{2}\vartheta^2 \, \overline{R^2 \, \mathrm{e}^{-\beta \vartheta R}}) - 1$$

where $0 \leqslant \alpha \leqslant 1$, $0 \leqslant \beta \leqslant 1$. Further,

$$\sigma^2 = \tfrac{1}{2}\vartheta^2 (\overline{R^2 \, \mathrm{e}^{\alpha \vartheta R}} + \overline{R^2 \, \mathrm{e}^{-\beta \vartheta R}} + \tfrac{1}{2}\vartheta^2 \, \overline{R^2 \, \mathrm{e}^{\alpha \vartheta R}} \, \overline{R^2 \, \mathrm{e}^{-\beta \vartheta R}})$$
$$= O(\vartheta^2 \, \bar{R}^2) \quad \text{if} \quad \vartheta^2 \, \bar{R}^2 \to 0,$$

by Schwarz' inequality.

Therefore $\qquad \sigma^2 = O(\vartheta^2 \, \bar{R}^2) \quad \text{if} \quad \vartheta^2 \, \bar{R}^2 \to 0.$ $\qquad$ Q.E.D.

COROLLARY.

$$\gamma^2 = O\{\vartheta^2 \overline{(R - \bar{R})^2}\} \quad \text{if} \quad \vartheta^2 \overline{(R - \bar{R})^2} \to 0.$$

Proof. Repeat the proof of the theorem for the Hamiltonian function $\qquad\qquad H(x) - \bar{R}.$

Note. If the parameter ϑ or the variance of the interaction energy R is sufficiently small, then, by Theorem 20.5, sum functions are approximately ergodic and approximately constant. The above condition does not exclude large values of the interaction energy; it is not its largest value which matters, but, instead, the distribution of its values as a whole, characterized by the variance.

For large values of ϑ, the correlation coefficient γ need not be small. So, in this case, sum functions need no longer be approximately constant and ergodic. Therefore, *the larger is the value of ϑ, the less definite are the former propositions about sum functions.*

21.6. The actual computation of Boltzmann's density $w^1(x^1)$ from Gibbs's density const. $\exp[-\vartheta H(x)]$ is difficult when the potential function contains interaction terms which cannot be neglected. Possibly in such a case the following proposition may facilitate the computation for systems of equivalent mass-points.

THEOREM. *Let a mechanical system of n equivalent mass-points have the Hamiltonian function*

$$H(x) \equiv \sum_{\nu=1}^{n} \frac{p^{\nu} p^{\nu}}{2m} + \sum_{\nu=1}^{n} V^1(q^{\nu}) + \sum_{1 \leqslant \lambda < \nu \leqslant n} V^{12}(q^{\lambda}, q^{\nu}),$$

where $\qquad\qquad V^{12}(q^{\lambda}, q^{\nu}) \equiv V^{12}(q^{\nu}, q^{\lambda}),$

and the canonic probability density const. $\exp[-\vartheta H(x)]$. *If, for the probability density of any pair of particles* (λ, ν),

$$w^{12}(x^\lambda, x^\nu) = w^1(x^\lambda)\, w^1(x^\nu),$$

then the probability $w^1(x^1)$ *of any particle satisfies the non-linear integral equation*

$$w^1(x^1) = \text{const.} \exp\left\{-\vartheta\left[\frac{p^1 p^1}{2m} + V^1(q^1) + \right.\right.$$
$$\left.\left. + (n-1)\int_{\Gamma^2} V^{12}(q^1, q^2)\, w^1(x^2)\, dx^2\right]\right\},$$

and the probability density for its position q^1 *in the real space,*

$$w^1_q(q^1) \equiv \int_{\Gamma^1_p} w^1(p^1, q^1)\, dp^1,$$

satisfies the integral equation

$$w^1_q(q^1) = \text{const.} \exp\left\{-\vartheta\left[V^1(q^1) + \right.\right.$$
$$\left.\left. + (n-1)\int_{\Gamma^2_q} V^{12}(q^1, q^2)\, w^1_q(q^2)\, dq^2\right]\right\}.$$

Proof. By Corollary 17.5 and Theorem 10.5, both sides of the integral equation for $w^1(x^1)$ are First Integrals of the equations of motion 17.5 for the first particle. Hence their quotient Q is a First Integral also. It depends on q only and not on p since, by Theorem 21.4,

$$w^1(x^1) = \text{const.} \exp\left\{-\vartheta\left[\frac{p^1 p^1}{2m} + V^*(q^1, \vartheta)\right]\right\}.$$

On account of the invariance of Q the derivative of $Q\{q^1(\overset{\circ}{x}, t)\}$ with respect to the time variable t must vanish identically.

Thus
$$\sum_{\kappa=1}^{3} \frac{\partial Q}{\partial q^1_\kappa}\, \dot{q}^1_\kappa \equiv 0,$$

or
$$\sum_{\kappa=1}^{3} \frac{\partial Q}{\partial q^1_\kappa}\, \frac{p^1_\kappa}{m} \equiv 0.$$

Hence, $\partial Q / \partial q_\kappa^1 \equiv 0$ and $Q \equiv$ const., and this implies the statements of the theorem.

Note. If there are (non-constant) interaction terms, the assumption of the theorem, that $w^{12} \equiv w^1 w^2$, never holds rigorously. Hence it is a fiction. That it is approximately fulfilled must be checked and made plausible by physical arguments before the theorem may be applied.

References

Similar (but different) considerations about sum functions are contained in Khindrin's book [23].

The solution of the integral equation for $wq^1(q^1)$ is one of the principal problems of stellar dynamics, cf.

[44] KURTH, R., *Introduction to the Mechanics of Stellar Systems*, Pergamon Press, London, 1957, or

[45] KURTH, R., General theory of spherical self-gravitating star systems in a steady state, *Astr. Nachr.*, **282**, 97, 1955.

For stellar systems, the potential $V^1(q^1)$ vanishes and the potential $V^{12}(q^1, q^2)$ is Newton's gravitational potential.

CHAPTER VII

STATISTICAL THERMODYNAMICS

§ 22. The equation of state

22.1. The following definitions are generalizations of the Definitions 17.7.

DEFINITIONS. Consider a system of n mass-points with the masses $m^1, m^2, \ldots, m^n$, the vectors of momentum $p^1, p^2, \ldots, p^n$, and the vectors of position $q^1, q^2, \ldots, q^n$. Let $w^\nu(x^\nu, t) \equiv w(p^\nu, q^\nu, t)$ be the probability density of the νth mass-point in its phase space Γ^ν, and

$$w_q^\nu(q^\nu, t) \equiv \int_{\Gamma_p^\nu} w^\nu(p^\nu, q^\nu, t)\, \mathrm{d}p^\nu$$

be the probability density of its position vector q^ν in the "position space" Γ_q^ν. Then define the *number density* $D(q', t)$ of the system at the point q' of the real space Γ_q' and at time t by

$$D(q', t) = \sum_{\nu=1}^n w_q^\nu(q', t);$$

define its *mass density* $\zeta(q', t)$ by

$$\rho(q', t) \equiv \sum_{\nu=1}^n m^\nu\, w_q^\nu(q', t);$$

and define its *pressure tensor* $P_{\kappa\lambda}(q', t)$ by

$$P_{\kappa\lambda}(q', t) \equiv \sum_{\nu=1}^n \frac{1}{m^\nu} \overline{(p_\kappa^\nu - \overline{p_\kappa^\nu}^{(q^\nu)})(p_\lambda^\nu - \overline{p_\lambda^\nu}^{(q^\nu)})}^{(q^\nu)}\, w_q^\nu(q', t).$$

Here, the symbol $\bar{g}^{(q^\nu)}$ denotes the conditional expectation value

$$\bar{g}^{(q^\nu)} \equiv \frac{\displaystyle\int_{\Gamma_p^\nu} g(p^\nu, q', t)\, w^\nu(p^\nu, q', t)\, \mathrm{d}p^\nu}{\displaystyle\int_{\Gamma_p^\nu} w^\nu(p^\nu, q', t)\, \mathrm{d}p^\nu}$$

for any function $g(x^\nu, t)$ such that all the integrals required in the definition exist. The *pressure* $P(q', t, \alpha)$ *in the direction* α, where $\alpha = (\alpha_1, \alpha_2, \alpha_3)$ and $|\alpha| = 1$, is defined by the quadratic form (with respect to α)

$$P(q', t, \alpha) \equiv \sum_{\kappa=1}^{3} \sum_{\lambda=1}^{3} P_{\kappa\lambda}(q', t) \, \alpha_\kappa \alpha_\lambda,$$

and the *mean pressure* $P_0(q', t)$ at the point q' is defined as the direction average

$$P_0(q', t) \equiv \frac{1}{4\pi} \int_\sigma \sum_{\kappa, \lambda} P_{\kappa\lambda} \, \alpha_\kappa \alpha_\lambda \, x \, d\alpha,$$

where $d\alpha$ denotes the element of area on the unit sphere σ. Thus

$$P_0(q', t) = \tfrac{1}{3}(P_{11} + P_{22} + P_{33}).$$

Note. The formula for P_0 is obtained without any calculation by considerations of symmetry: the direction averages of $\alpha_1\alpha_2$, $\alpha_2\alpha_3$ and $\alpha_3\alpha_1$ vanish, those of $\alpha_1\alpha_1$, $\alpha_2\alpha_2$ and $\alpha_3\alpha_3$ are equal, and the sum of the latter is 1.

22.2. THEOREM. *Let L' be any Lebesgue subset of the real space Γ'_q. Then, the phase average of the number of the particles in L' at the instant t is given by*

$$\int_{L'} D(q', t) \, dq',$$

and the phase average of the total mass of these particles is

$$\int_{L'} \rho(q', t) \, dq'.$$

(The symbols D and ρ have the meaning stipulated in the Definitions 22.1.)

For the proof, see the Definitions 22.1 and Note 20.4.

Note. Since

$$\int_{L'} D(q', t) \, dq'$$

can be regarded as the phase average of a certain sum function (see § 20.4), the actual number of particles N, in L', may be assumed to be approximately equal to the integral

$$\int_{L'} D \, dq'$$

if the (3-dimensional) measure of L' is not too small and the

144   AXIOMATICS OF STATISTICAL MECHANICS

correlation coefficient γ (as occurring in Theorem 20.5) is not too large. The same holds for the mass density $\rho(q', t)$.

22.3. THEOREM. *Assume that the probability density $w(x, t)$ of a system of n mass-points differs from zero only in a bounded subset of the phase space Γ, and that it is a continuous function of the phase point x. Further assume that an ideal plane passes through the point q' of the real space Γ'_q, the normal direction of which is $\alpha = (\alpha_1, \alpha_2, \alpha_3)$, $|\alpha| = 1$. Let S denote any measurable part of this plane such that it contains the point q' and its diameter (i.e. the supremum of all the mutual distances of any two points of S) has a positive finite value δ. Denote the (two-dimensional) measure of S by $|S|$, which is supposed to be positive also. Then the phase average of the component of the momentum p^ν in the direction α, carried by the νth particle through S during the interval of time $t \dots (t + \Delta t)$, is given by*

$$\frac{1}{m^\nu} \sum_{\kappa=1}^{3} \sum_{\lambda=1}^{3} \overline{p^\nu_\kappa p^\nu_\lambda}^{(q^\nu)} \{w^\nu_q(q', t)\, \alpha_\kappa \alpha_\lambda + o_{\Delta t}(1) + o_\delta(1)\} \, |S| \, \Delta t,$$

where $o_{\Delta t}(1)$ and $o_\delta(1)$ denote terms which tend towards zero if $\Delta t \to 0$ and $\delta \to 0$, respectively.

Proof. The phase average dealt with in the theorem is given by

$$\int_{B^\nu} \sum_{\kappa=1}^{3} p^\nu_\kappa \alpha_\kappa\, w^\nu(x^\nu, t)\, \mathrm{d}x^\nu,$$

where B^ν denotes that part of the space Γ^ν within which the point x^ν must be if the νth particle is to pass through the area S. Assume, only for convenience in the notation, that the direction of the normal vector α coincides with that of the positive 1-axis. Consider the case $p^\nu_1 \geqslant 0$ first. If the particle moves during the time interval $t \dots (t + \Delta t)$ in a straight line with constant velocity, it must, at time t, be in a certain cylinder C^ν in order to be able to pass through S. The base of this cylinder is the area S, its axis is parallel to the vector of momentum p^ν, its height is $(p^\nu_1/m^\nu)\, \Delta t$, and it is situated in the half-space $q'_1 \leqslant 0$. Thus its volume is $|S|\,(p^\nu_1/m^\nu)\, \Delta t$. In general, however, the particles do not move with constant velocity or in a constant direction. The deviation can be taken into account, in the expression for the volume of C^ν, by substituting $p^\nu_1 + O(\Delta t)$ for p^ν_1.

The procedure in the case $p_1^\nu \leqslant 0$ is similar. For the phase average under consideration, therefore, the following expression is obtained:

$$\int_{\substack{C_+^\nu \\ p_1\nu \geqslant 0}} p_1^\nu w^\nu(x^\nu, t) \, \mathrm{d}x^\nu + \int_{\substack{C_-^\nu \\ p_1\nu \leqslant 0}} p_1^\nu w^\nu(x^\nu, t) \, \mathrm{d}x^\nu$$

$$= \int_{p_1\nu \geqslant 0} p_1^\nu \left\{ \int_{C_+^\nu} w^\nu(p^\nu, q^\nu, t) \, \mathrm{d}q^\nu \right\} \mathrm{d}p^\nu$$

$$+ \int_{p_1\nu \leqslant 0} p_1^\nu \left\{ \int_{C_-^\nu} w^\nu(p^\nu, q^\nu, t) \, \mathrm{d}q^\nu \right\} \mathrm{d}p^\nu$$

$$= \int_{\Gamma_p\nu} p_1^\nu \{w^\nu(p^\nu, q^\nu, t) + o_{\Delta t}(1) + o_\delta(1)\} \, |S| \left\{ \frac{p_1^\nu}{m^\nu} + O(\Delta t) \right\} \Delta t \, \mathrm{d}p_1^\nu$$

(since $w^\nu(x^\nu, t)$ depends continuously on x^ν). For a general direction α, the component $\sum_{\kappa=1}^{3} p_\kappa^\nu \alpha_\kappa$ of the momentum p^ν must be substituted for p_1^ν, and this completes the proof of the theorem.

Notes. For an area S moving with the velocity $\bar{p}^{\nu(q^\nu)}/m^\nu$, the expression

$$\frac{1}{m^\nu} \sum_{\kappa=1}^{3} \sum_{\lambda=1}^{3} \overline{(p_\kappa^\nu - \overline{p_\kappa^{\nu(q^\nu)}}) (p_\lambda^\nu - p_\lambda^{\nu(q^\nu)})^{(q^\nu)}} w_q^\nu(q', t) \, \alpha_\kappa \, \alpha_\lambda$$

(i.e. by Definition 22.1, the partial pressure of the νth particle in the direction α) can be interpreted in a similar fashion. Now, in general, the velocities $\overline{p^{\nu(q^\nu)}}/m^\nu$, $\nu = 1, 2, ..., n$, are different. Therefore it is more useful in practical applications to replace Definition 22.1 by

$$P_{\kappa\lambda} = \sum_{\nu=1}^{n} \frac{1}{m^\nu} \overline{(p_\kappa^\nu - m^\nu v_\kappa)(p_\lambda^\nu - m^\nu v_\lambda)}^{(q^\nu)}$$

where $v = (v_1, v_2, v_3)$ denotes the velocity of the area S. It should be observed, however, that this definition is not the natural generalization of Definition 17.7, as was suggested by Euler's equation 17.9.

The pressure has not been defined, in the above, by the momentum conferred by the particle upon a material area S. If the particle experiences an elastic reflection by S, then the momentum conferred on S is given by

$$\frac{2}{m^{\nu}} \int\limits_{\substack{Z^{\nu} \\ p_1{}^{\nu} \geqslant 0}} p_1^{\nu} p_1^{\nu} \, w^{\nu}(x^{\nu}, t) \, \mathrm{d}p^{\nu}$$

or, for a general direction α,

$$\frac{2}{m^{\nu}} \sum_{\kappa=1}^{3} \sum_{\lambda=1}^{3} \int\limits_{\substack{3 \\ \Sigma \, p_c{}^{\nu}\alpha_c \geqslant 0 \\ c=1}} p_{\kappa}^{\nu} p^{\nu} \, w^{\nu}(x^{\nu}, t) \, \mathrm{d}p^{\nu} \, \alpha_{\kappa} \, \alpha_{\lambda} \, |\, S \,| \, \Delta t$$

apart from terms $o_{\Delta t}(1)$ and $o_{\delta}(1)$. This expression refers to the actually observed pressure of the phenomenological theory of gases, and can be different from the pressure defined by

$$\frac{1}{m^{\nu}} \sum_{\kappa, \, \lambda} \overline{p_{\kappa}^{\nu} p_{\nu}^{\lambda}}^{(q^{\nu})} \, \alpha_n \, \alpha_{\lambda}.$$

(Cf. § 22.8.)

22.4. THEOREM AND DEFINITION. *If, for a system of n mass-points, all the n expressions*

$$\frac{1}{m^{\nu}} \overline{(p_{\kappa}^{\nu} - \overline{p_{\kappa}^{\nu}}^{(q^{\nu})}) (p_{\lambda}^{\nu} - \overline{p_{\lambda}^{\nu}}^{(q^{\nu})})}^{(q^{\nu})}, \quad \nu = 1, 2, \dots, n, \qquad (*)$$

are equal, for each pair of indices κ, λ, and their common value is $T_{\kappa\lambda}(q', t)$, then the pressure tensor $P_{n\lambda}$ can be represented in the form

$$P_{\kappa\lambda} = D \cdot T_{\kappa\lambda}$$

where $D(q', t)$ denotes the number density of the system. $T_{\kappa\lambda}$ is called the temperature tensor of the system; the expression $\sum\limits_{\kappa, \, \lambda} T_{\kappa\lambda} \alpha_c \alpha_{\lambda}$ is called its temperature at the point q' and at the time t, in the direction α. The expression $\frac{1}{2} \sum\limits_{\kappa, \, \lambda} T_{\kappa\lambda} \alpha_n \alpha_{\lambda}$ gives the conditional expectation value (with respect to the position q') of the component of the kinetic energy of the νth particle in direction α, if its velocity is reckoned from the conditional expectation value of the velocity (with respect to the position of the particle). Both the quadratic forms $\sum\limits_{\kappa, \, \lambda} T_{\kappa\lambda} \alpha_n \alpha_{\lambda}$, and $\sum\limits_{\kappa, \, \lambda} P_{\kappa\lambda} \alpha_n \alpha_{\lambda}$ of α are positive-definite. The direction average of $\sum\limits_{\kappa, \, \lambda} T_{\kappa\lambda}, \alpha_n \alpha_{\lambda}$, that is the value $\frac{1}{3}(T_{11} + T_{22} + T_{33})$, will be called the mean temperature T_0 of the system at q'. The mean pressure P_0, the mean temperature

T_0 and the number density D are connected by the "Equation of State",

$$P_0 = DT_0.$$

22.5. For which mechanical systems does a temperature exist, i.e. under what conditions are all the expressions (*) of § 22.4 equal? They are always so if all the particles are equivalent. Another sufficient condition is given by:

THE EQUIPARTITION THEOREM. *A system of n mass-points governed by the Hamiltonian function*

$$H(x) \equiv \sum_{\nu=1}^{n} \frac{p^{\nu} p^{\nu}}{2m^{\nu}} + V(q)$$

and described by a canonic probability density

$$w(x) \equiv \text{const.} \exp\left[-\vartheta H(x)\right], \quad \vartheta \text{ const.} > 0,$$

possesses a temperature, which is independent of position and direction and the value of which is $1/\vartheta$. If L and $L^1, ..., L^n$ denote the kinetic energies of the system and of the single particles, and their phase averages are denoted by bars, then

$$\frac{1}{\vartheta} = \frac{2}{3} \frac{\overline{L}}{n} = \frac{2}{3} \overline{L^{\nu}}, \quad \nu = 1, ..., n.$$

Note 1. The term "equipartition" shall indicate that, to each particle, the same amount of kinetic energy is attributed "on the average". The temperature appears here as the phase average of the sum function $\frac{2}{3}L/n$ and can, therefore, be approximated by its instantaneous values or its time average (cf. 20.5). The actual measurements give time averages.

The *proofs* of the theorem and of its following generalization are immediate consequences of the definitions and assumptions.

COROLLARY. Let the Hamiltonian function of a mechanical system be

$$H(x) \equiv \sum_{\lambda=1}^{l} (p^{\lambda} - c^{\lambda}) . S^{\lambda}(q^{\lambda}) (p^{\lambda} - c^{\lambda}) + V(q)$$

where $x^{\lambda} = (p^{\lambda}, q^{\lambda})$ denotes a $2k$-dimensional component of the phase vector x, c^{λ} is a k-dimensional function only of q^{λ}, and $S^{\lambda}(q^{\lambda})$ is a positive-definite quadratic matrix of k columns, depending also only on q^{λ}. Assume the probability density of the system to be canonic:

$$w(x) \equiv \text{const.} \exp[-\vartheta H(x)].$$

Then

$$\overline{p^{\lambda(q^\lambda)}} = c^\lambda$$

and

$$\overline{(p^\lambda - c^\lambda) \cdot S^\lambda(q^\lambda)(p^\lambda - c^\lambda)}^{(q^\lambda)} = \frac{k}{2\vartheta}, \quad \lambda = 1, 2, ..., l.$$

Note 2. The Equipartition Theorem is sometimes formulated in the following fashion: the energy is uniformly distributed over all coordinates with respect to which the Hamiltonian function is quadratic. This statement, however, need not be true, as is shown by the following example. A mechanical system consisting of n harmonic oscillators with weak interactions has the Hamiltonian function

$$H(x) \equiv \tfrac{1}{2}x^2 + \text{negligible interaction term.}$$

Its equations of motion read

$$\left.\begin{array}{l} \dot{p}_\kappa^\nu = -q_\kappa^\nu \\ \dot{q}_\kappa^\nu = +p_\kappa^\nu \end{array}\right\} \begin{array}{l} \nu = 1, ..., n, \\ \kappa = 1, 2, 3. \end{array}$$

There are the $3n$ time-independent First Integrals $p_\kappa^\nu p_\kappa^\nu + q_\kappa^\nu q_\kappa^\nu$. Now define the First Integral $F(x)$ by

$$F(x) \equiv \sum_{\kappa=1}^{3} \sum_{\nu=1}^{n} c_\kappa (p_\kappa^\nu p_\kappa^\nu + q_\kappa^\nu q_\kappa^\nu),$$

where c_1, c_2 and c_3 are positive constants, and put

$$w(x) \equiv \text{const.} \, e^{-\vartheta F(x)}, \quad \vartheta = \text{const.} > 0,$$

in analogy to Gibbs's canonic density. Then

$$\overline{p_\kappa^\nu p_\kappa^{\nu(q^\nu)}} = \overline{(p_\kappa^\nu p_\kappa^\nu)} = \frac{1}{c_\kappa \vartheta}, \quad \begin{cases} \nu = 1, ..., n, \\ \kappa = 1, 2, 3. \end{cases}$$

Hence the Equipartition Theorem holds here only if $c_1 = c_2 = c_3$, i.e. if the probability density $w(x)$ is a function only of the Hamiltonian function $H(x)$.

The same is true, for example, for a system of equivalent rigid bodies whose mass distributions have rotational symmetry and which do not exert (appreciable) interactions on each other. The momenta corresponding to the rotations around the axes of symmetry are First Integrals of the Hamiltonian

equations of motion. Hence the Equipartition Theorem need
not apply to them. It is certainly valid, however, if $w(x)$ is a
(suitable) function of $H(x)$ only.

22.6. DEFINITIONS AND THEOREM. Let a system of n mass-
points consist of a classes $\alpha = 1, 2, ..., a$ of equivalent particles.
To each class α, there correspond a partial number density
$D^{(\alpha)}(q',t)$, a partial pressure tensor $P^{(\alpha)}_{\kappa\lambda}(q',t)$, and a *partial
temperature tensor* $T^{(\alpha)}_{\kappa\lambda}(q',t)$, the latter being defined by

$$T^{(\alpha)}_{\kappa\lambda}(q',t) \equiv \frac{1}{m^{(\alpha)}} \overline{(p^{(\alpha)}_\kappa - \overline{p^{(\alpha)(q^\alpha)}_\kappa})(p^{(\alpha)}_\lambda - \overline{p^{(\alpha)(q^\nu)}_\lambda})}^{(q^\nu)}.$$

Then, for each class α,

$$P^{(\alpha)}_{\kappa\lambda} = D^{(\alpha)}\, T^{(\alpha)}_{\kappa\lambda}.$$

For the total pressure tensor, the following equation of state holds:

$$P_{\kappa\lambda} = \sum_{\alpha=1}^{a} D^{(\alpha)}_{\kappa\lambda}\, T^{(\alpha)}_{\kappa\lambda}.$$

Notes. The equations of state of § 22.4 and § 22.6 are identi-
ties. They have verifiable physical contents only if the pressure
defined statistically is identified with the pressure measured
dynamically. These two quantities are, in general, however, at
best approximately equal. Under the assumption of elastic
reflections, an exact expression for the observed pressure was
given in Note 22.3. It seems that, under the same assumption,
the same expression holds for "molecules" consisting of several
"atoms" and for particles of finite dimensions also.

Even if the phenomenological and the statistical pressure
coincide, the differences between observations and the above
theoretical laws can be appreciable for low temperatures,
according to Note 21.5.

22.7. ("VIRIAL") THEOREM. *Let a mechanical system of* n
mass-points have the Hamiltonian function

$$H(x) \equiv L(p) + V(q) \equiv \frac{1}{2}\sum_{\nu=1}^{n} \frac{p^\nu p^\nu}{2m^\nu} + V(q)$$

where the potential function $V(q)$ *is assumed not to depend on the
time variable* t *and to be homogenous in* q *of the order* $\alpha \neq -2$.
If $\overset{0}{x}$ *is the phase-point of the system at time zero and* $E = H(\overset{0}{x})$
is its energy, then, for the time averages $\hat{L}(\overset{0}{x},t)$ *and* $\hat{V}(\overset{0}{x},t)$ *of the*

kinetic and potential energies $L(p)$ and $V(q)$,

$$\left.\begin{aligned} \hat{L}(\mathring{x}, t) &= \frac{\alpha}{2+\alpha} E + \frac{1}{2+\alpha} \frac{p \cdot q}{t} \\ \hat{V}(\mathring{x}, t) &= \frac{2}{2+\alpha} E - \frac{1}{2+\alpha} \frac{p \cdot q}{t} \end{aligned}\right\} \quad \text{if} \quad t > 0.$$

Here the symbol $(p.q)$ on the right-hand sides denotes the solution vector $\chi(\mathring{x}, t)$ of the equations of motion.

Proof. By Lagrange's Identity 12.8 and the Energy Integral 10.5,

$$\frac{d}{dt}(p.q) = \frac{d^2}{dt^2} \sum_1^n \frac{1}{2} m^\nu q^\nu q^\nu = 2L - \alpha V$$

$$= \begin{cases} 2L - \alpha(E - L), \\ 2(E - V) - \alpha V. \end{cases}$$

Now the theorem is obtained by an integration with respect to t, and division by t.

COROLLARY. If the trajectory $x = \chi(\mathring{x}, t)$, $t \geqslant 0$ is a bounded subset of the phase space Γ, then, for $t \to 0$, the limits $\hat{L}_\infty(\mathring{x})$ and $\hat{V}_\infty(\mathring{x})$ exist, and

$$\left.\begin{aligned} \hat{L}_\infty(\mathring{x}) &= \frac{\alpha}{2+\alpha} H(\mathring{x}), \\ \hat{V}_\infty(\mathring{x}) &= \frac{2}{2+\alpha} H(\mathring{x}). \end{aligned}\right\}$$

Note. If there is a canonic probability density for the system, then, by Theorem 22.5, there is a temperature T, which depends neither on the position nor on the direction and is given by

$$T = \frac{1}{\vartheta} = \frac{2}{3} \frac{\bar{L}}{n}.$$

Since $L(p)$ is a sum function, it may be expected that, for a large number, n, of particles and at high temperatures, $\bar{L}$ equals $\hat{L}$ approximately, in the sense that $\bar{L}/\hat{L}$ differs only little from unity. Hence, in the same sense,

$$T \approx \frac{2}{3} \frac{\alpha}{2+\alpha} \frac{E}{n}.$$

22.8. PROPOSITION. Let a system of n particles have the time-independent Hamiltonian function

$$H(x) \equiv L(p) + V(q) + U(q),$$

where
$$L(p) \equiv \frac{1}{2} \sum_1^n \frac{p^\nu p^\nu}{2m^\nu}$$

is its kinetic energy, $V(q)$ the potential of its internal interactions, which is supposed to be homogenous in q of order $\alpha \neq -2$, and

$$U(q) \equiv b \sum_{\nu=1}^n \left(\frac{|q^\nu|}{R} \right)^\beta,$$

where R, b and β are positive constants, and β is supposed to be very much larger than unity. $U(q)$ is the potential representing a spherical wall of the radius R which encloses the system. Further, let the system have a canonic probability density

$$w(x) = \frac{1}{\phi} \exp\left[-\vartheta H(x) \right],$$

where
$$\phi = \int_\Gamma \exp\left[-\vartheta H(x) \right] dx,$$

such that its actual energy E equals the phase average $\bar{H}$ of its Hamiltonian function $H(x)$ approximately. Then, for unit area and unit time, a momentum $\tilde{P}$ is conferred on the wall "on the average" (i.e. in the area average of the time average) where $\tilde{P}$ is given by

$$\tilde{P} \approx \frac{2+\alpha}{3} \frac{\hat{L}}{\frac{4}{3}\pi R^3} - \frac{\alpha}{3} \frac{E}{\frac{4}{3}\pi R^3}, \tag{i}$$

$$\tilde{P} \approx \frac{2+\alpha}{2} \tilde{D}T - \frac{\alpha}{3} \tilde{E}, \tag{ii}$$

or
$$\tilde{P} \approx \frac{2+\alpha}{2} \tilde{D}T \left(1 - \frac{2}{3} \frac{\alpha}{2+\alpha} \frac{T}{n} \frac{\partial \ln \phi}{\partial T} \right). \tag{iii}$$

Here T denotes the temperature $1/\vartheta$ of the system, $\tilde{D}$ is its mean number density $n / \frac{4}{3}\pi R^3$, and $\tilde{E}$ is its mean energy density $E / \frac{4}{3}\pi R^3$.

Argument. The relation

$$2\hat{L} - \alpha\hat{V} - \beta\hat{U} = \frac{pq}{t}$$

6

can be demonstrated in a manner similar to that of § 12.7.
Hence, by the elimination of $\hat{V}$ by means of the Energy Integral

$$\hat{L} + \hat{V} + \hat{U} = E,$$

it follows that $\qquad \hat{U} \approx \dfrac{2+\alpha}{\beta-\alpha}\,\hat{L} - \dfrac{\alpha}{\beta-\alpha}\,E \qquad (*)$

for sufficiently large values of t. Now, by Euler's Identity
(12.7),

$$\beta U = \sum_{\nu=1}^{n} q^{\nu}\,U^{\nu},$$

where $\qquad U^{\nu} \equiv \left(\dfrac{\partial U}{\partial q_1^{\nu}},\ \dfrac{\partial U}{\partial q_2^{\nu}},\ \dfrac{\partial U}{\partial q_3^{\nu}}\right).$

The force exerted by the wall on the νth particle is $-U^{\nu}$;
hence U^{ν} is the force exerted by the particle on the wall. Since
the vectors U^{ν} and q^{ν} are collinear (the origin of coordinates
being chosen in the centre of the spherical vessel),

$$q^{\nu}\,U^{\nu} = |q^{\nu}|\,|U^{\nu}|.$$

Now the force U^{ν} is appreciable only if $|q^{\nu}| \gtrsim R$. For $|q^{\nu}| > R$,
it increases so rapidly with increasing distance of the particle
from the centre that $|q^{\nu}|$ will never be considerably larger
than R. Therefore,

$$\beta\hat{U} = \sum_{\nu} (q^{\nu}\,U^{\nu})^{\wedge} = \sum_{\nu} (|q^{\nu}|\,|U^{\nu}|)_{\wedge}$$

$$\approx R\sum_{\nu} |U^{\nu}{}_{(|q^{\nu}|\approx R)}|^{\wedge}$$

$$\approx R\,.\,4\pi R^2\,\tilde{P}.$$

By eliminating $\hat{U}$ from this equation and equation (*), the
equations (i) and (ii) of the proposition are obtained. When
$\bar{H}$ is then substituted for E in equation (ii) and expressed by
means of the relations

$$\bar{H} = \frac{1}{\phi}\int_{\Gamma} H(x)\exp\left[-\vartheta H(x)\right]\mathrm{d}x$$

$$= -\frac{1}{\phi}\frac{\partial\phi}{\partial\vartheta} = -\frac{\partial}{\partial\vartheta}\ln\phi$$

$$= T^2\frac{\partial}{\partial T}\ln\phi,$$

equation (iii) is obtained.

Note. The assumption that the vessel is spherical appears essential. Otherwise considerable local deviations of the pressure from its area average may be possible.

§ 23. The fundamental laws of thermodynamics

23.1. GENERAL ASSUMPTIONS. In this section an ensemble of mechanical systems of the following kind will be considered. To each system there corresponds a Hamiltonian function $H(x,\lambda)$ and a "truncated canonic probability density"

$$w(x,\lambda,\vartheta) = \frac{1}{\phi}\exp[-\vartheta H(x,\lambda)]\,\delta_J(x),$$

where

$$\phi(\lambda,\vartheta) \equiv \int_J \exp[-\vartheta H(x,\lambda)]\,dx,$$

J is a (non-empty) bounded open invariant subset of the phase space Γ, $\delta_J(x)$ is its characteristic function, $\lambda = (\lambda_1,\lambda_2,...,\lambda_s)$ is an s-dimensional parameter which is variable within a given sphere K of the s-dimensional vector space R^s. The function $H(x,\lambda)$ is supposed to possess partial derivatives with respect to $\lambda_1,...,\lambda_s$ which are continuous functions of (x,λ). The function $H(x,\lambda)$ shall be common to all the systems, which are, however, assumed to be distinguished by different vectors λ and different temperatures $T = 1/\vartheta$. The parameter ϑ is variable in an open interval of the positive ϑ-axis. It is supposed that, to each admitted vector (λ,ϑ), there corresponds exactly one system of the ensemble.

Notes. The substitution of the canonic probability density by the above truncated canonic probability density is an unessential restriction, from the physical point of view. It has been introduced for mathematical convenience since it implies the existence of all the integrals and derivatives needed in what follows, so that no particular assumptions need be made about them.

In practical applications, there is no such infinite set of mechanical systems with each system uniquely characterized by its $(s+1)$-dimensional vector (λ,ϑ). There is, instead, only one system of which the vector (λ,ϑ) is varied in course of time by suitable experimental manipulations. (For example, the volume of a gas is altered.) Thus (ϑ, λ) appears as a given function of the time t which we suppose to possess a piecewise continuous derivative $(\dot{\lambda}, \dot{\vartheta})$ with respect to t. It should be noted, however, that when $(\dot{\lambda}, \dot{\vartheta}) \neq 0$, the function $w\{x, \lambda(t), \vartheta(t)\}$ is not a probability density, since then it is not a First Integral of the equations of motion $\dot{x} = X(x, \lambda)$ (in which λ has to be regarded as a constant). For,

$$
\frac{\partial}{\partial t} w\{\chi(\mathring{x}, t), \lambda(t), \vartheta(t)\} = \sum_\nu \left(\frac{\partial w}{\partial x_\nu} X_\nu\right)_{x = \chi(\mathring{x}, t)} + \sum_\sigma \frac{\partial w}{\partial \lambda_\sigma} \dot{\lambda}_\sigma + \frac{\partial w}{\partial \vartheta} \dot{\vartheta}
$$

$$
= \sum_\sigma \frac{\partial w}{\partial \lambda_\sigma} \dot{\lambda}_\sigma + \frac{\partial w}{\partial \vartheta} \dot{\vartheta},
$$

by Liouville's Equation 17.2, where the right-hand side is, in general, different from zero if $(\dot{\lambda}, \dot{\vartheta}) \neq 0$. After a transition of the system from a "state" (λ^1, ϑ^1) to another "state" (λ^2, ϑ^2), the parameters (λ, ϑ) must be kept fixed and the system must be given time to adapt itself to the new probability density $w(x, \lambda^2, \vartheta^2)$. The period needed for this will, in general, be at least of the order of the time scale (cf. § 19.1). Only after this adaptation, the phase averages based on the probability density $w(x, \lambda^2, \vartheta^2)$ may be expected, in the sense of § 20, to describe the system with a sufficient approximation.

23.2. DEFINITIONS. ϑ and the components of λ are called *thermodynamical variables*. The vector (λ, ϑ) corresponding to any particular system of the ensemble is named the *thermodynamical state* of this system. Functions which depend only on λ and ϑ are said to be *thermodynamical functions*.

The *internal energy* of a system is defined as the phase average

$$
\bar{H}(\lambda, \vartheta) = \int_\Gamma H(x, \lambda) \, w(x, \lambda, \vartheta) \, \mathrm{d}x
$$

of its Hamiltonian function $H(x, \lambda)$. Further, let τ be a real parameter varying in the closed interval $0 \ldots 1$, and let (λ, ϑ) be an $(s+1)$-dimensional function of τ which possesses piecewise continuous derivatives with respect to τ, and for which

$$
\left.\begin{aligned}
\lambda(0) &= \lambda^1, & \lambda(1) &= \lambda^2, \\
\vartheta(0) &= \vartheta^1, & \vartheta(1) &= \vartheta^2.
\end{aligned}\right\}
$$

If $\vartheta^1 = \vartheta^2 = \vartheta$, the line integral

$$A_c(\vartheta) \equiv \int_0^1 \sum_{\sigma=1}^s \frac{\overline{\partial H}}{\partial \lambda_\sigma} \frac{\mathrm{d}\lambda_\sigma(\tau)}{\mathrm{d}\tau} \, \mathrm{d}\tau,$$

where

$$\frac{\overline{\partial H}}{\partial \lambda_\sigma} = \int_\Gamma \frac{\partial H}{\partial \lambda_\sigma} w(x, \lambda, \vartheta) \, \mathrm{d}x,$$

is said to be the *work* done on the system in the transition from the state (λ^1, ϑ) to the state (λ^2, ϑ) along the curve c, defined by $\lambda = \lambda(\tau)$. The expression

$$\{\bar{H}(\lambda^2, \vartheta) - \bar{H}(\lambda^1, \vartheta)\} - A_c(\vartheta)$$

is called the *heat* transferred to the system by the same transition. For the transition from (λ, ϑ^1) to (λ, ϑ^2), the vector λ being kept fixed, the heat is defined by the expression

$$\bar{H}(\lambda, \vartheta^2) - \bar{H}(\lambda, \vartheta^1).$$

The integral

$$\phi(\lambda, \vartheta) \equiv \int_J \exp\left[-\vartheta H(x, \lambda)\right] \mathrm{d}x$$

{or, for an untruncated canonic density

$$\phi(\lambda, \vartheta) \equiv \int_\Gamma \exp\left[-\vartheta H(x, \lambda)\right] \mathrm{d}x\}$$

is called the *partition integral* of the system (or, rather, of the ensemble of systems) and the logarithm

$$\Psi(\lambda, \vartheta) \equiv \ln \phi(\lambda, \vartheta)$$

is called its *thermodynamical potential*.

Notes. The definition of work is made plausible by the following consideration. The integral

$$\int_0^1 \sum_{\sigma=1}^s \frac{\partial H}{\partial \lambda_\sigma} \frac{\mathrm{d}\lambda_\sigma(\tau)}{\mathrm{d}\tau} \, \mathrm{d}\tau$$

is the difference of the energies $H(x, \lambda^2) - H(x, \lambda^1)$ if the phase-point x is kept fixed, i.e. it is the work needed for the transition from (x, λ^1) to (x, λ^2). Therefore, in order to obtain a definition of work independent of the phase-point x, it seems reasonable to use the phase average. This, however, cannot well be applied to finite differences of the thermodynamical states since the probability density also depends on λ. But it can be applied to "infinitesimal" differences and this application yields the above definition.

The concept of heat has been defined in such a manner that the First Law of Thermodynamics (as given by the phenomenological theory) is valid by definition; the identity

$$\bar{H}(\lambda^2, \vartheta^2) - \bar{H}(\lambda^1, \vartheta^1) = [\bar{H}(\lambda^2, \vartheta^2) - \bar{H}(\lambda^2, \vartheta^1)]$$
$$+ [\bar{H}(\lambda^2, \vartheta^1) - \bar{H}(\lambda^1, \vartheta^1) - A_c(\vartheta^1)]$$
$$+ A_c(\vartheta^1)$$

can be interpreted as

change of internal energy = heat transferred by change of temperature,

$$+ \text{heat transferred by change of } \lambda,$$

$$+ \text{work},$$

and this is the First Law of Thermodynamics. In the following, a "differential formulation" of this Law will be given, which is an immediate consequence of the above definitions.

23.3. First Law of Thermodynamics. *Under the assumptions* 23.1, *the heat* δQ *and the work* δA *needed for the transition from the thermodynamical state* (λ, ϑ) *to the thermodynamical state* $(\lambda + \delta\lambda, \vartheta + \delta\vartheta)$ *are given by*

$$\delta Q = \sum_{\sigma=1}^{s} \left(\frac{1}{\vartheta} \frac{\partial \Psi}{\partial \lambda_\sigma} - \frac{\partial^2 \Psi}{\partial \vartheta \, \partial \lambda_\sigma} \right) \delta\lambda_\sigma - \frac{\partial^2 \Psi}{\partial \vartheta^2} \delta\vartheta + o(|\delta\lambda|) + o(\delta\vartheta),$$

$$\delta A = - \sum_{\sigma=1}^{s} \frac{1}{\vartheta} \frac{\partial \Psi}{\partial \lambda_\sigma} + o(|\delta\lambda|) + o(\delta\vartheta),$$

where $\Psi(\lambda, \vartheta)$ *is the thermodynamical potential of the system. The corresponding change of the internal energy*

$$\bar{H}(\lambda, \vartheta) \equiv - \frac{\partial}{\partial \vartheta} \Psi(\lambda, \vartheta)$$

is given by

$$\delta\bar{H} = - \sum_{\sigma=1}^{s} \frac{\partial^2 \Psi}{\partial \vartheta \, \partial \lambda_\sigma} \delta\lambda_\sigma - \frac{\partial^2 \Psi}{\partial \vartheta^2} \delta\vartheta + o(|\delta\lambda|) + o(\delta\vartheta),$$

so that $\delta\bar{H} = \delta A + \delta Q + o(|\delta\lambda|) + o(\delta\vartheta).$

23.4. Second Law of Thermodynamics. *Under the assumptions* 23.1, *a thermodynamical function* $S(\lambda, \vartheta)$, *the "entropy",*

exists such that its complete differential $\delta S(\lambda, \vartheta)$ *differs from* $\vartheta \delta Q$
only by terms of the order $o(|\delta\lambda|) + o(\delta\vartheta)$. *It is given by*

$$S(\lambda, \vartheta) \equiv \Psi(\lambda, \vartheta) - \vartheta\frac{\partial\Psi(\lambda, \vartheta)}{\partial\vartheta}.$$

Proof. Compute δS from the above expression for S and compare the result with 23.2.

COROLLARY. The integral

$$\int_{(\lambda^1, \vartheta^1)}^{(\lambda^2, \vartheta^2)} \frac{dQ}{T} \quad (\text{where } T = 1/\vartheta),$$

extended over any piecewise differentiable curve (see 23.3) connecting the points (λ^1, ϑ^1) and (λ^2, ϑ^2) of R^{s+1}, is independent of the particular choice of this curve. The heat ΔQ needed for the transition from (λ^1, ϑ^1) to (λ^2, ϑ^2) is $T^* . (S^2 - S^1)$, where $S^1 = S(\lambda^1, \vartheta^1)$, $S^2 = S(\lambda^2, \vartheta^2)$ and T^* is a temperature between T^1 and T^2. If $T_2 > T_1$, the corresponding work, ΔA, is given by

$$\Delta A = \bar{H}^2 - \bar{H}^1 - T^*(S^2 - S^1)$$

$$\geqslant F^2 - F^1,$$

where $$F = \bar{H} - TS.$$

Proof. First,

$$\int_{(\lambda^1, \vartheta^1)}^{(\lambda^2, \vartheta^2)} \vartheta\, dQ = \int_{(\lambda^1, \vartheta^1)}^{(\lambda^2, \vartheta^2)} dS = S^2 - S^1,$$

by the theorem. Secondly,

$$\Delta Q = \int_{(\lambda^1, \vartheta^1)}^{(\lambda^2, \vartheta^2)} dQ = \int_{(\lambda^1, \vartheta^1)}^{(\lambda^2, \vartheta^2)} T\, dS = T^*(S^2 - S^1),$$

by the Mean Value Theorem of Integral Calculus (cf. § 8.3).
Finally,

$$\Delta A = \bar{H}^2 - \bar{H}^1 - \Delta Q$$

$$= \bar{H}^2 - \bar{H}^1 - T^*(S^2 - S^1)$$

$$= (\bar{H}^2 - T^* S^2) - (\bar{H}^1 - T^* S^1)$$

$$\geqslant (\bar{H}^2 - T^2 S^2) - (\bar{H}^1 - T^1 S^1).$$

Q.E.D.

Note. If $\Delta A < 0$, then $(-\Delta A)$ is the work gained by the transition. It is not larger than $F^1 - F^2$. Therefore, the thermodynamical function

$$F(\lambda, \vartheta) \equiv \bar{H}(\lambda, \vartheta) - \frac{1}{\vartheta} S(\lambda, \vartheta)$$

is called the *free energy*, and the function $TS \equiv (1/\vartheta) S(\lambda, \vartheta)$ is said to be the *bound energy* attached to the state (λ, ϑ).

23.5. THEOREM. *Let each mechanical system of the ensemble 23.1 have two components x' and $x'' = x/x'$ without mutual interaction, so that*

$$H(x, \lambda) \equiv H'(x', \lambda) + H''(x'', \lambda),$$

and let "partial entropy functions" $S'(\lambda, \vartheta)$ and $S''(\lambda, \vartheta)$ correspond to these components. Then

$$S(\lambda, \vartheta) = S'(\lambda, \vartheta) + S''(\lambda, \vartheta).$$

The statement follows immediately from the expression 23.4 for the entropy.

Note. The complete differential of each function $\{S(\lambda, \vartheta) +$ an arbitrary constant$\}$ equals $\vartheta \delta Q$ (apart from higher-order terms). But only if the additive constant vanishes is the entropy additive (in the sense of the theorem). It was chosen intentionally so that entropy should be additive. It appears that this property is possible, but necessary. In phenomenological thermodynamics, it seems sometimes to be taken for granted that entropy is additive.

Example. A monatomic ideal gas, enclosed in a vessel G of volume $|G|$, can be attributed the Hamiltonian function

$$\frac{pp}{2m} + \prod_{\nu=1}^{n} \frac{1}{\delta_G(q^\nu)} - 1.$$

Its potential is 0 if all the particles are within G, and is ∞ if at least one particle is outside. Thus it is a mathematical description of the walls of G. Replacing it by a suitable continuous approximation, we may apply the above results. For example, from 23.5 and 23.7, it follows immediately that, in this approximation,

$$\Psi = n\{\ln|G| + \tfrac{3}{2}\ln(2\pi mT)\},$$
$$S = n\{\ln|G| + \tfrac{3}{2}[1 + \ln(2\pi mT)]\}.$$

The general relations

$$\bar{H} = -\frac{\partial \Psi}{\partial \vartheta},$$

$$\left.\frac{\overline{\partial H}}{\partial \lambda_\sigma} = -\frac{1}{\vartheta}\frac{\partial \Psi}{\partial \lambda_\sigma}\right\}$$

of Theorem 23.3 yield, in combination with the Equation of State of 22.4,

$$\bar{H} = \tfrac{3}{2}nT,$$

$$\left.\frac{\partial \bar{H}}{\partial |G|} = -\frac{n}{\vartheta}\frac{1}{|G|} = -DT = -P\right\}$$

if the volume $|G|$ of the vessel is taken as a parameter λ. This is admissible if the walls of G are movable, for example by means of a piston. Thus

$$\delta A = -P\delta|G|$$

and

$$\delta Q = \tfrac{3}{2}n\delta T + P\delta|G|.$$

The specific heats $c_{|G|}$ and c_p for constant volume and constant pressure are defined by

$$c_{|G|} = \left(\frac{\delta Q}{\delta T}\right)_{\delta|G|=0},$$

$$\left.c_p = \left(\frac{\delta Q}{\delta T}\right)_{\delta p=0}.\right\}$$

Hence

$$c_{|G|} = \tfrac{3}{2}n$$

and, on account of the equations

$$P.\delta|G| = \delta(P|G|) - |G|\delta P$$

$$= \delta(nT) - |G|\delta P$$

(by the Equation of State),

$$c_p = \tfrac{5}{2}n,$$

so that, finally,

$$c_p - c_{|G|} = n,$$

$$\left.\frac{c_p}{c_{|G|}} = \tfrac{5}{3}.\right\}$$

23.6. LEMMA (LAPLACE'S INTEGRATION FORMULA). *Let B be a bounded open subset of R^n which contains the point 0, let*

$\bar{B}$ *be its closure,* $g(x)$ *a (scalar) function which is continuous in* $\bar{B}$, *and* $h(x)$ *a function which possesses continuous second-order derivatives*

$$\frac{\partial^2 h(x)}{\partial x_\lambda \, \partial x_\nu} \equiv 2h_{\lambda\nu}(x)$$

in B *and of which a proper minimum in* $\bar{B}$ *exists for* $x = 0$. *Let the quadratic form*

$$\sum_{\lambda=1}^{n} \sum_{\nu=1}^{n} h_{\lambda\nu}(0)\, x_\lambda x_\nu$$

be positive-definite, denote its determinant $\det|h_{\lambda\nu}(0)|$ *by* Δ, *and let* ϑ *be a positive parameter. Then*

$$\int_B g(x)\exp[-\vartheta h(x)]\,dx$$
$$= \exp[-\vartheta h(0)]\left(\frac{\pi^n}{\vartheta^n\,\Delta}\right)^{\frac{1}{2}}[g(0)+o(1)] \quad \text{if} \quad \vartheta\to\infty.$$

Proof. Let S_δ be an n-dimensional sphere with centre at 0 and radius δ. Then, for sufficiently small values of δ, S_δ is a subset of B, and

$$\int_B g(x)\exp[-\vartheta h(x)]\,dx = \int_{S_\delta}\cdots + \int_{B-S_\delta}\cdots.$$

The last integral can be estimated in the following fashion

$$\left|\int_{B-S_\delta} g(x)\exp[-\vartheta h(x)]\,dx\right| \leqslant \sup_{x\in B}|g(x)|\exp[-\vartheta \min_{|x|=\delta} h(x)]\mu B,$$

since, for sufficiently small values of δ, $h(x)$ is in $\bar{B}-S_\delta$ not smaller than

$$\min_{|x|=\delta} h(x).$$

Now assume $h(x) \geqslant 0$. (Otherwise, replace $h(x)$ by

$$h(0) + \{h(x) - h(0)\}$$

and apply the following derivation to $\{h(x)-h(0)\}$.) Then

$$\left|\int_{B-S_\delta} g\exp(-\vartheta h)\,dx\right| \leqslant \sup|g|\exp[-\vartheta h(0)]$$
$$\times \exp\{-\vartheta.c\delta^2[1+o(1)]\}\mu B \quad \text{for} \quad \delta\to 0, \quad (*)$$

where c denotes a positive constant. Put $\delta = \vartheta^{-\frac{1}{4}}$, for sufficiently large values of ϑ. Then, if $\vartheta \to \infty$, the right-hand side of the inequality (*) and, therefore, the integral

$$\int_{B-S_\delta} g \exp(-\vartheta h) \, dx$$

tends towards zero. In fact,

$$\int_{B-S_\delta} g \exp(-\vartheta h) \, dx = O\{\exp[-\vartheta h(0) - c\vartheta^{\frac{1}{4}}]\} \quad \text{if} \quad \vartheta \to \infty.$$

For

$$\int_{S_\delta} g \exp(-\vartheta h) \, dx$$

we obtain

$$\int_{S_\delta} g \exp(-\vartheta h) \, dx = [g(0) + o_\delta(1)] \exp[-\vartheta h(0)] \times$$

$$\times \int_{S_\delta} \exp\left\{-\vartheta \sum_{\lambda, \nu} h_{\lambda\nu}(0) x_\lambda x_\nu [1 + o_\delta(1)]\right\} dx$$

$$\text{(for } \delta \to 0)$$

$$= [g(0) + o_\delta(1)] \exp[-\vartheta h(0)] \int_{S_\delta} \exp\left[-\vartheta \sum_{\lambda, \nu} h_{\lambda\nu}(0) x_\lambda x_\nu\right] dx$$

$$= [g(0) + o_\delta(1)] \exp[-\vartheta h(0)] \left\{\int_{R^n} \cdots - \int_{R^n - S_\delta} \cdots\right\}.$$

The above estimate of the integral $\int_{B-S_\delta} \ldots$ applies to the integral $\int_{R^n - S_\delta} \ldots$ also, so that $\int_{R^n - S_\delta} \ldots \to 0$ if $\vartheta \to \infty$. The integral $\int_{R^n} \ldots$ is calculated by an orthogonal linear transformation of the quadratic form $\vartheta \Sigma h_{\lambda\nu}(0) x_\lambda x_\nu$ on its principal axes. Taking the invariance of the determinant Δ with respect to orthogonal transformations into account, we obtain

$$\int_{S_\delta} g \exp(-\vartheta h) \, dx = [g(0) + o(1)] \exp[-\vartheta h(0)] \times$$

$$\times \left[\left(\frac{\pi^n}{g^n \Delta}\right)^{\frac{1}{2}} + O\{\exp[-\vartheta h(0) - c\vartheta^{\frac{1}{4}}]\}\right]$$

$$= [g(0) + o(1)] \exp[-\vartheta h(0)] \left(\frac{\pi^n}{\vartheta^n \Delta}\right)^{\frac{1}{2}}$$

162   AXIOMATICS OF STATISTICAL MECHANICS

for $\vartheta \to \infty$. Therefore

$$\int_B g \exp(-\vartheta h)\,dx = [g(0)+o(1)]\exp[-\vartheta h(0)]\left(\frac{\pi^n}{\vartheta^n \Delta}\right)^{\frac{1}{2}}+$$
$$+ O\{\exp[-\vartheta h(0)-c\vartheta^{\frac{1}{2}}]\}$$
$$= [g(0)+o(1)]\exp[-\vartheta h(0)]\left(\frac{\pi^n}{\vartheta^n \Delta}\right)^{\frac{1}{2}}.$$

Q.E.D.

COROLLARY. If the function $g(x)$ possesses, in B, continuous partial derivatives with respect to $x_1, \ldots, x_n$ of the jth order and if it vanishes with all the derivatives of 1st, 2nd, $\ldots, (j-1\text{st})$ order at the point 0, then

$$\int_B g(x) \exp[-\vartheta h(x)]\,dx = O(\vartheta^{-n/2-j/2}) \quad \text{if} \quad \vartheta \to \infty.$$

For the proof, approximate $g(x)$ in S_δ by a (homogeneous) polynomial of jth order, according to Taylor's Theorem. The rest of the proof is similar to that of the theorem.

23.7. THIRD LAW OF THERMODYNAMICS. *Let, under the assumptions 23.1, the Hamiltonian function $H(x,\lambda)$ have the proper minimum 0 at $x = 0$; let the quadratic form:*

$$2\sum_{\alpha=1}^{n}\sum_{\beta=1}^{n}\left[\frac{\partial^2 H(x,\lambda)}{\partial x_\alpha \partial x_\beta}\right]_{x=0} x_\alpha x_\beta$$

be positive-definite, and denote its determinant by $\Delta(\lambda)$. Then the following asymptotic relations hold for the thermodynamical potential $\Psi(\lambda,\vartheta)$, the entropy $S(\lambda,\vartheta)$, the internal energy $\bar{H}(\lambda,\vartheta)$, the bound energy $(1/\vartheta)S(\lambda,\vartheta)$ and the free energy $F(\lambda,\vartheta)$:

$$\Psi\left(\lambda,\frac{1}{T}\right) = \frac{n}{2}\ln(\pi T) - \frac{1}{2}\ln\Delta(\lambda) + o(1),$$

$$S\left(\lambda,\frac{1}{T}\right) = \frac{n}{2}\ln T + O(1),$$

$$\bar{H}\left(\lambda,\frac{1}{T}\right) = O(T),$$

$$TS\left(\lambda,\frac{1}{T}\right) = \frac{n}{2}T\ln T + O(T),$$

$$F\left(\lambda,\frac{1}{T}\right) = -\frac{n}{2}T\ln T + O(T)$$

if $T = 1/\vartheta \to 0$.

Proof. By 23.2,

$$\phi = \int_J \exp\left[-\vartheta H(x)\right] dx = \left(\frac{\pi^n}{\vartheta^n \Delta}\right)^{\frac{1}{2}} [1 + o(1)],$$

by Theorem 23.6, and this implies the statement about Ψ. Further,

$$\phi \bar{H} = \int_J H \exp\left[-\vartheta H(x)\right] dx = O(\vartheta^{-n/2-1}),$$

by Corollary 23.6; hence

$$\bar{H} = O(\vartheta^{-1}),$$

as stated in the theorem. Since

$$S = \Psi + \vartheta \bar{H}$$

by Theorem 23.4, $S = \dfrac{n}{2} \ln T + O(1).$

The statements about TS and F are now immediate consequences.

Notes. In phenomenological thermodynamics, both the propositions,

$$\left.\begin{array}{l} \lim_{T \to 0} (TS) = 0, \\[2mm] \lim_{T \to 0} \dfrac{\partial}{\partial T}(TS) = 0, \end{array}\right\} \tag{*}$$

are regarded as contents of the Third Law. The first proposition is a consequence of the asymptotic relation for TS stated in the theorem. It will now be checked whether the second proposition holds also within the frame of classical statistical mechanics. That is, $(\partial/\partial T)(TS)$ will be estimated.

Now

$$\frac{\partial}{\partial T}(TS) = S + T\frac{\partial S}{\partial T} = S + \frac{1}{\vartheta}\frac{\partial S}{\partial T}$$

$$= S + \frac{1}{\vartheta}\frac{\partial S}{\partial \vartheta}\frac{\partial \vartheta}{\partial T}$$

$$= S - \vartheta\frac{\partial S}{\partial \vartheta}.$$

Since $S = \Psi - \vartheta\dfrac{\partial \Psi}{\partial \vartheta},$

by Theorem 23.3,

$$\frac{\partial S}{\partial \vartheta} = -\vartheta \frac{\partial}{\partial \vartheta}\frac{\partial \Psi}{\partial \vartheta} = \vartheta \frac{\partial \bar{H}}{\partial \vartheta}$$

by Theorem 23.3. Thus

$$\frac{\partial}{\partial T}(TS) = S - \vartheta^2 \frac{\partial \bar{H}}{\partial \vartheta}.$$

Now

$$\frac{\partial \bar{H}}{\partial \vartheta} = -\frac{\partial}{\partial \vartheta}\frac{\partial \Psi}{\partial \vartheta} = -\frac{\partial}{\partial \vartheta}\left(\frac{1}{\phi}\frac{\partial \phi}{\partial \vartheta}\right) = -\left\{\frac{1}{\phi}\frac{\partial^2 \phi}{\partial \vartheta^2} - \left(\frac{1}{\phi}\frac{\partial \phi}{\partial \vartheta}\right)^2\right\}$$

$$= -(\overline{H^2} - \bar{H}^2) = -\overline{(H - \bar{H})^2}.$$

(The equation $$\overline{H^2} = \frac{1}{\phi}\frac{\partial^2 \phi}{\partial \vartheta^2}$$

follows immediately from Definition 23.2 of ϕ.) By Corollary 23.6,

$$\overline{H^2} = O(\vartheta^{-2}),$$

therefore

$$\frac{\partial \bar{H}}{\partial \vartheta} = O(\vartheta^{-2}),$$

and, finally, $\quad \dfrac{\partial}{\partial T}(TS) = S + O(1) = \dfrac{n}{2}\ln T + O(1),$

and $\qquad\qquad \lim_{T\to 0}\dfrac{\partial}{\partial T}(TS) = -\infty.$

This contradicts the statement (*) of phenomenological thermodynamics. Its empirical foundation is the observation that, at low temperatures, the bound energy varies very slowly with temperature. This fact, however, is already implied by the asymptotic relation $TS \to 0$ if $T \to 0$.

Another formulation of the phenomenological Third Law reads

$$\lim_{T\to 0}\left\{S\left(\lambda^2, \frac{1}{T}\right) - S\left(\lambda^1, \frac{1}{T}\right)\right\} = 0.$$

Theorem 23.7, however, yields only the weaker statement that

$$\frac{S\left(\lambda^2, \dfrac{1}{T}\right) - S\left(\lambda^1, \dfrac{1}{T}\right)}{S\left(\lambda^1, \dfrac{1}{T}\right)} = O\left(\frac{1}{\ln T}\right) \quad \text{if} \quad T \to 0.$$

A similar asymptotic relation is obtained for the bound energy by multiplying the numerator and denominator of the left-hand side by the factor T. Thus, the following proposition holds:

COROLLARY. For sufficiently low temperatures, the relative changes of the entropy and the bound energy of a system, produced by isothermal variations of its thermodynamical state, are arbitrarily small.

§ 24. Entropy and probability

24.1. THEOREM. *Under the assumptions* 23.1, *the entropy* $S(\lambda, \vartheta)$ *and the truncated canonic probability density* $w(x, \lambda, \vartheta)$ *satisfy the relation*

$$S(\lambda, \vartheta) = -\overline{\ln w(x, \lambda, \vartheta)} = -\int_J w(x, \lambda, \vartheta) \ln w(x, \lambda, \vartheta)\, dx.$$

Proof.
$$w = \frac{\exp(-\vartheta H)}{\phi} \quad \text{if} \quad x \in J,$$

$$-\ln w = \vartheta H + \ln \phi, \quad -\overline{\ln w} = -\vartheta \frac{\partial \Psi}{\partial \vartheta} + \Psi,$$

since
$$\overline{H} = -\frac{\partial \Psi}{\partial \vartheta}$$

by Theorem 23.3. Hence, by Theorem 23.4,

$$-\overline{\ln w} = S.$$

Q.E.D.

Note. The same formula holds, under suitable assumptions, if the probability density is canonic.

COROLLARY. Let the Hamiltonian function of an ensemble of mechanical systems (cf. 23.1) be

$$H(x) \equiv \sum_{\kappa=1}^{k} H^\kappa(x^\kappa, \lambda) + R(x, \lambda),$$

where
$$|R(x, \lambda)| \leqslant r = \text{const.}$$

Assume that there is a canonic probability density $w(x, \lambda, \vartheta)$ and that the phase averages of the functions $H^1, ..., H^k$ and R

exist. Then

$$S(\lambda, \vartheta) = - \sum_{\kappa=1}^{k} \overline{\ln w^{\kappa}(x^{\kappa}, \lambda, \vartheta)} + O(r\vartheta)$$

$$= - \sum_{\kappa=1}^{k} \int_{\Gamma^{\nu}} w^{\kappa} \ln w^{\kappa} \, dx^{\kappa} + O(r\vartheta) \quad \text{if} \quad r\vartheta \to 0.$$

Here, $w^{\kappa}(x^{\kappa}, \lambda, \vartheta)$ denotes the probability density of the component x^{κ} in its phase space Γ^{κ}.

Proof.
$$w^{\kappa} = \frac{\exp(-\vartheta H^{\kappa})}{\phi^{\kappa}} [1 + O(r\vartheta)],$$

where
$$\phi^{\kappa} = \int_{\Gamma^{\kappa}} \exp(-\vartheta H^{\kappa}) \, dx^{\kappa}.$$

Therefore
$$\phi = \prod_{\kappa=1}^{k} \phi^{\kappa} . [1 + O(r\vartheta)], \quad \Psi = \sum_{\kappa=1}^{k} \Psi'^{\kappa} + O(r\vartheta)$$

(where $\Psi'^{\kappa} = \ln \phi^{\kappa}$), and

$$-\overline{\ln w} = \int_{\Gamma} (\vartheta H + \Psi) w \, dx = \sum_{\kappa} \int_{\Gamma} (\vartheta H^{\kappa} + \Psi'^{\kappa}) w \, dx + O(r\vartheta)$$

$$= - \sum_{\kappa} \int_{\Gamma} [\ln w^{\kappa} + O(r\vartheta)] w \, dx + O(r\vartheta)$$

$$= - \sum_{\kappa} \int_{\Gamma^{\nu}} \ln w^{\kappa} w^{\kappa} \, dx + O(r\vartheta).$$

Q.E.D.

Notes. The assumption that $|R|$ is small is more restricted than is actually necessary, and has been introduced only for convenience in estimating the errors. In fact, the assumption that $\overline{R^2}$ or $\overline{(R - \bar{R})^2}$ is small is sufficient. (See Note 21.5.)

For similar reasons of convenience, truncation of the canonic probability density has now been abandoned.

According to Theorem 21.5, the sum function

$$\sum_{\kappa} \ln w^{\kappa} \{\chi(\mathring{x}, t), \lambda, \vartheta\}$$

may be expected, for large values of k and $1/\vartheta$, to be approximately constant and equal to $-S(\lambda, \vartheta)$.

If all the components $x^1, \dots, x^k$ of the system are equivalent, then

$$S(\lambda, \vartheta) = -k \int_{\Gamma^1} w^1 \ln w^1 \, dx^1.$$

The expression on the right-hand side is sometimes used to explain the observed approach of mechanical systems towards statistical equilibrium. This explanation will be discussed in what follows.

24.2. DEFINITIONS. Let $x^1, x^2, \ldots, x^k$ be equivalent components of a mechanical system with the time-independent probability density $w(x)$. Let Γ' be a space which is congruent with $\Gamma^1, \ldots, \Gamma^n$ and in which a probability density $w'(x')$ is defined by $w'(x') \equiv w^1(x')$, where $w^1(x^1)$ is the probability density of the first component x^1 in its phase space Γ^1. Suppose that Γ' is divided into a "cells" $B_1, B_2, \ldots, B_a$, i.e. into a Lebesgue subsets no two of which have common points and the sum of which is Γ^1. Assume that all the cells have the same probability

$$\int_{B_\alpha} w'(x') \, dx' = \frac{1}{a}, \quad \alpha = 1, 2, \ldots, a.$$

Let $N_\alpha(x)$ be the number of all those components which, for a given phase-point x, lie in B_α (i.e. the number of those points $x^1, x^2, \ldots, x^k$ of which the congruent images x' in Γ' lie in B'. See Note 20.4 and Corollary 20.5.) The set of the a numbers $N_1(x), N_2(x), \ldots, N_a(x)$ is called the *configuration* belonging to the phase-point x, the expression

$$\Omega(x) \equiv \frac{k!}{N_1(x)! \ldots N_a(x)!} \left(\frac{1}{a}\right)^{N_1(x)} \cdots \left(\frac{1}{a}\right)^{N_a(x)}$$

$$= \frac{k!}{N_1(x)! \ldots N_a(x)!} \left(\frac{1}{a}\right)^k$$

is called the *fictitious probability of the configuration* $(N_1, \ldots, N_a)$, and the sum function

$$h(x) \equiv -k \sum_{\alpha=1}^{a} \frac{N_\alpha(x)}{k} \ln \frac{N_\alpha(x)}{k}$$

is said to be the *Gibbsian function of this configuration*.

Notes. The fictitious configuration probability $\Omega(x)$ can be interpreted as the probability for obtaining the configuration $(N_1, \ldots, N_a)$ by k "independent" casts of the components $x^1, \ldots, x^k$ into the space Γ'. As is indicated by the name, this interpretation, however, is only a fiction: the true probability of the configuration $(N_1, \ldots, N_a)$ is given by an integral over

$w(x)$ extended over the set of all the points x of Γ which imply the configuration $(N_1, ..., N_a)$. (It is the sum of the intersections of certain cylindric sets, as becomes evident after a moment's reflection.) The true and the fictitious probabilities of the configuration $(N_1, ..., N_a)$ are necessarily equal only if

$$w(x) = \prod_{\kappa=1}^{k} w^\kappa(x^\kappa),$$

that is (according to § 21.1), only if there are no interactions between the components of the system.

The notion of configuration can be used for a precise definition of the concept of the macroscopic state of a mechanical system (cf. Note 19.2). This can be defined, for example, as a configuration in the real space.

24.3. THEOREM. *Gibbs's function $h(x)$ and the fictitious probability $\Omega(x)$ of a configuration are connected by the asymptotic relation*

$$h(x) = [\ln \Omega(x) + k \ln a][1 + o(1)] \quad \text{if} \quad \min_{1 \leqslant \alpha \leqslant a} N_\alpha(x) \to \infty.$$

Proof.

$$\ln \Omega(x) = \ln (k!) - \sum_{\alpha=1}^{a} \ln (N_\alpha!) - k \ln a.$$

From the curve "$\ln x$ against x" it is read off that

$$\int_1^k \ln x \, dx < \sum_{\kappa=1}^{k} \ln \kappa = \ln (k!) < \int_2^{k+1} \ln x \, dx \quad \text{if} \quad k \geqslant 2.$$

Hence

$$\ln (k!) = k \ln \frac{k}{e} \left[1 + O\!\left(\frac{1}{k}\right) \right] \quad \text{for} \quad k \to \infty,$$

since

$$\int \ln x \, dx = x \ln x - x + \text{const.}$$

Thus,

$$\ln \Omega(x) = k \ln \frac{k}{e} \cdot \left[1 + O\!\left(\frac{1}{k}\right) \right]$$

$$- \sum_\alpha N_\alpha \ln \frac{N_\alpha}{e} \left[1 + O\!\left(\frac{1}{N_\alpha}\right) \right] - k \ln a.$$

On account of

$$k = \sum_\alpha N_\alpha,$$

it follows that

$$\ln \Omega(x) = -\sum_\alpha N_\alpha \ln \frac{N_\alpha}{k} + O(\ln k) + \sum_\alpha O(\ln N_\alpha) - k \ln a,$$

and this implies the statement of the theorem, as is seen by a comparison with the definition of the function $h(x)$ in § 24.2.

Notes. There are generalizations of Definitions 24.2 and Theorem 24.3 if the space Γ' is divided into cells $B_1, ..., B_a$ of unequal probabilities.

If, in the case of equal probabilities, the constant factor $(1/a)^k$ is omitted in the definition of $\Omega(x)$, then the term $k \ln a$ in the asymptotic equation of the theorem drops out. In the physical literature, the expression

$$\frac{k!}{N_1! ... N_a!}$$

is called the "thermodynamical probability" of the configuration $(N_1, ..., N_a)$. It is not, however, actually a probability in the sense of § 14, even less than the fictitious probability $\Omega(x)$. If the sets $B_1, ..., B_a$ have unequal probabilities, a variable factor of $\Omega(x)$, depending on the phase-point x, is omitted to give the "thermodynamical probability".

24.4. THEOREM. The function

$$h = -k \sum_{\alpha=1}^{a} \frac{N_\alpha}{k} \ln \frac{N_\alpha}{k}$$

of the positive continuous variables $N_1, N_2, ..., N_a$, subjected to the condition that $\sum_{\alpha=1}^{a} N_\alpha = k$, possesses a maximum, $k \ln a$, for $N_\alpha = k/a$, $\alpha = 1, 2, ..., a$. Now, *under the assumptions* 21.5 *for the Hamiltonian function* $H(x)$ *and the probability density* $w(x)$ *of a mechanical system, let* $h(x)$ *be Gibbs's function,* $\chi(\overset{\circ}{x}, t)$ *be the general solution of the equations of motion,* $R(x)$ *be the interaction potential,* $1/\vartheta$ *be the temperature, a be the number of cells* $B_1, ..., B_a$ *of equal probability into which the space* Γ' *is divided, and* ϵ *be a positive constant smaller than* $1/\ln a$. *Then, at any instant t,*

$$P[\max_{x \in \Gamma} h(x) - h\{\chi(\overset{\circ}{x}, t)\} \geqslant \epsilon \max_{x \in \Gamma} h(x)]$$

$$\leqslant \frac{(a-1)a}{\epsilon \ln a} \left[\frac{1}{k} + O(\vartheta \sqrt{\overline{R^2}}) \right] \quad \text{if} \quad \vartheta^2 \overline{R^2} \to 0$$

where $P[...]$ denotes the probability of the set of all the points $\overset{\circ}{x}$ for which the relation in the square brackets holds.

Proof. The maximum of h is found by differentiation. From

$$\max_{x \in \Gamma} h(x) = k \sum_{\alpha} \frac{1}{a} \ln a$$

and

$$h(x) = -k \sum_{\alpha} \frac{N_{\alpha}}{k} \ln \frac{N_{\alpha}}{k},$$

it follows that

$$0 \leqslant \frac{\max h - h(x)}{\max h} = \frac{\sum\limits_{\alpha} (1 + \nu_{\alpha}) \ln (1 + \nu_{\alpha})}{a \ln a}$$

where ν_{α}, $\alpha = 1, ..., a$, is defined by

$$\frac{N_{\alpha}}{k} = \frac{\bar{N}_{\alpha}}{k} (1 + \nu_{\alpha}) = \frac{1}{a} (1 + \nu_{\alpha}).$$

By the Mean Value Theorem of Differential Calculus,

$$\ln (1 + \nu_{\alpha}) = \frac{\nu_{\alpha}}{1 + \eta_{\alpha} \nu_{\alpha}}, \quad 0 \leqslant \eta_{\alpha} \leqslant 1,$$

if $|\nu_{\alpha}| \leqslant \sqrt{(\epsilon . \ln a)} < 1$. Hence

$$\ln (1 + \nu_{\alpha}) \leqslant \nu_{\alpha}$$

and

$$(1 + \nu_{\alpha}) \ln (1 + \nu_{\alpha}) \leqslant \nu_{\alpha} + \nu_{\alpha}^2,$$

for these values of ν_{α}. Since

$$\sum_{\alpha} \nu_{\alpha} = 0,$$

it follows that

$$\frac{\max h - h(x)}{k \ln a} \leqslant \frac{\sum\limits_{\alpha} \nu_{\alpha}^2}{a \ln a} \leqslant \epsilon,$$

if

$$|\nu_{\alpha}| = \frac{|N_{\alpha} - \bar{N}_{\alpha}|}{\bar{N}_{\alpha}} \leqslant \sqrt{(\epsilon . \ln a)}.$$

Therefore,

$$P[\max h - h(\chi) \leqslant \epsilon \max h]$$
$$\geqslant P[| N_1 - \bar{N}_1| \leqslant \bar{N}_1 \sqrt{(\epsilon . \ln a)}, ..., | N_a - \bar{N}_a| \leqslant \bar{N}_a \sqrt{(\epsilon . \ln a)}]$$
$$\geqslant 1 - \sum_{\alpha=1}^{a} P[| N_{\alpha} - \bar{N}_{\alpha}| > \bar{N}_{\alpha} \sqrt{(\epsilon \ln a)}].$$

(The last inequality is a consequence of the fact that the sum of all the sets denoted by square brackets is the entire phase space Γ.) By Corollary 20.5 and Theorem 21.5,

$$-P[|N_\alpha - \bar{N}_\alpha| \geqslant \bar{N}_\alpha \sqrt{(\epsilon \ln a)}] \geqslant -\frac{a-1}{\epsilon . \ln a}\left[\frac{1}{k} + O(\vartheta \sqrt{\bar{R^2}})\right].$$

The statement of the theorems is now obtained by inserting the right-hand side into the last but one inequality.

Notes. This theorem is a precise version of Gibbs's "*H*-theorem" (*h*-theorem, in our notation). It states that, in course of time, the function $h\{\chi(\overset{\circ}{x},t)\}$ tends towards its maximum. In fact, the probability that $h\{\chi(\overset{\circ}{x},t)\}$ is, at any moment t, considerably smaller than $\max\limits_{x \in \Gamma} h(x)$ is small. Therefore it is improbable that $h\{\chi(x,t)\}$ decreases considerably in course of time. It is true an increase supposes that $h(\overset{\circ}{x})$ differs appreciably from $\max h(x)$, and the probability of this is also small. Therefore it seems that the following assumptions have to be made for Gibbs's proposition. Let the system be in a state, at time 0, which is not a state of statistical equilibrium, and assume that, after a sufficiently long interval of time, the system approaches such a state (cf. § 19). Then it is improbable that, for sufficiently large values of t, the value $h\{\chi(x,t)\}$ differs from $\max\limits_{x \in \Gamma} h(x)$ considerably. (The probabilities have to be related to the probability density corresponding to the final state of equilibrium.) The initial difference $\max\limits_{x \in \Gamma} h(x) - h(\overset{\circ}{x})$, however, may be (but need not be) large. In such a case the function $h\{\chi(x,t)\}$ in fact approaches its maximum from a lower initial value.

The value of the fictitious configuration probability $\Omega(x)$ which corresponds to the maximum of Gibbs's function $h(x)$ is approximately 1, by Theorem 24.3. In the case just described, the initial value $\Omega(\overset{\circ}{x})$ may be considerably smaller. Thus the system develops then in such a fashion that its fictitious configuration probability $\Omega[\chi(x,t)]$ increases.

All these considerations, however, are based only on plausibility. It is quite conceivable that the set of all the points $\overset{\circ}{x}$ for which $\Omega(\overset{\circ}{x}) \ll 1$ is such that its phase image at any time t does not belong to the set of phase-points x for which $\Omega(x) \approx 1$.

Since this idea can neither be proved nor refuted, and since the set for which $\Omega(x) \approx 1$ has a probability approximately equal to unity, the application of Rule 15.1 offers a refuge (truly an *asylum ignorantiae*): it is improbable that these points do not belong to the set for which $\Omega(x) \approx 1$; therefore $h\{\chi(\overset{\circ}{x},t)\}$ is likely to increase.

This presumable behaviour of the functions $h(x)$ and $\Omega(x)$ is by no means specific to them. Let, for instance, $f(x)$ be a sum function of which the phase average $\bar{f}$ is positive, and define a function $g(x)$ by

$$g(x) = 1 - \left\{\frac{f(x) - \bar{f}}{\bar{f}}\right\}^2.$$

Then $g(x)$ (and every strictly monotonic increasing function of $g(x)$) is likely to tend towards its maximum, in the above sense.

Example. Let an ideal monotonic gas (see § 23.5) be enclosed in a vessel G_1 of volume $|G_1|$. Remove, at time 0, a sliding-partition so that the gas can expand into a comprehensive vessel G_2 of volume $|G_2|$. Suppose that G_1 is divided into the sets $A_1, ..., A_{a_1}$, and G_2 is divided into the sets $A_1, ..., A_{a_1}$, $A_{a_1+1}, ..., A_{a_2}$, all of equal volume. Define the cells B_α of Definition 24.2 by the Cartesian products

$$B_\alpha = A_\alpha \times \Gamma'_p, \quad \alpha = 1, ..., a_2,$$

where Γ'_p denotes the space of momenta corresponding to the real space Γ'_q. With respect to the final time-independent probability density, all the sets $B_1, ..., B_{a_2}$ have the same probability $1/a_2$. Assume that, before the removal of the sliding-partition, the system was also in a state of statistical equilibrium. Then the probabilities of the sets $B_1, ..., B_{a_1}$ were $1/a_1$, and those of the sets $B_{a_1+1}, ..., B_{a_2}$ were zero. Hence for $t < 0$ the value of the function $h(x)$ was very likely to be approximately $n \ln a_1$ (where n denotes the number of the particles). Immediately after the removal of the sliding-partition, $h(x)$ has the same value with respect to the division of G_2 into the cells $A_1, ..., A_{a_2}$ as it had with respect to the division of G_1 into the cells $A_1, ..., A_{a_1}$, immediately before the removal. But the maximum of $h(x)$ is now $n . \ln a_2$, and so it is likely that, in course of time, $h\{\chi(\overset{\circ}{x},t)\}$ approaches this value, increasing by $n \ln (a_2/a_1)$.

24.5. *Entropy and Gibbs's function.* If the vessel G_1 had been extended to G_2 not by the sudden removal of the sliding-partition, but by a (sufficiently slow) continuous motion of the walls, the entropy S increases by the same amount, for according to Example 23.5,

$$S(G_2, \vartheta) - S(G_1, \vartheta) = n \cdot \ln \frac{|G_2|}{|G_1|}$$

$$= n \ln \frac{a_2}{a_1},$$

$$= \max_{x \in \Gamma} h(x) - h(\overset{\circ}{x})$$

$$\approx \ln \frac{\max \Omega(x)}{\Omega(\overset{\circ}{x})}.$$

Similar equations are sometimes called "Boltzmann's Postulate" and regarded as fundamental relations between "thermo-dynamical probability" and entropy. Occasionally the expressions

$$S \approx - k \int_{\Gamma^1} w^1 \ln w^1 \, dx^1$$

for the entropy (see Corollary 24.1) and

$$h(x) = - k \sum_{\alpha} \frac{N_\alpha}{k} \ln \frac{N_\alpha}{k}$$

for Gibbs's function (see Definition 24.2) are also identified in the physical literature. However, in general, this is not admissible: the function $h(x)$ probably differs but little from its maximum, which is given by

$$k \ln a = - k \sum_{\alpha=1}^{a} \frac{1}{a} \ln \frac{1}{a}$$

$$= - k \sum_{\alpha=1}^{a} \int_{B_\alpha} w^1(x^1) \, dx^1 . \ln \int_{B_\alpha} w^1(x^1) \, dx^1,$$

whilst $$S(\lambda, \vartheta) \approx - k \sum_{\alpha=1}^{a} \int_{B_\alpha} w^1(x^1, \lambda, \vartheta) \ln w^1(x^1, \lambda, \vartheta) \, dx^1.$$

Only in exceptional cases (similar to that of the ideal gas) are both expressions equal. Hence Boltzmann's Postulate seems to hold only in such exceptional cases.

Moreover, the functions $h(x)$ and $S(\lambda, \vartheta)$ refer to quite different circumstances. The entropy is applied to "reversible" encroachments on the system, while Gibbs's function refers to irreversible encroachments. The word "irreversible" means that the chance of the first encroachment being cancelled by the opposite encroachment is very small. Thus, for instance, the gas of Example 24.4 will collect in G_1 again and again, by Poincaré's Recurrence Theorem 12.2; but the probability of this, $(a_1/a_2)^n$, is always very small and so is the chance of re-establishing the original state of the system by closing the vessel G_1 with the sliding-partition at the appropriate instant. Processes which are irreversible, in the sense discussed, exist neither in "free nature" (in general) nor in closed systems left to themselves. They exist (essentially) only under experimental conditions in which the experimenter brings about a quite improbable state (by, for example, opening the partition). The system will seldom return to this state again. It is only interference such as this which introduces an irreversible aspect into the process.

If the removal of the sliding-partition is reversed by a reversible encroachment, e.g. by the motion of a piston, then work must be done against the gas pressure P. This work is given by

$$-\int_{|G_2|}^{|G_1|} P \, d|G| = -nT \int_{|G_2|}^{|G_1|} \frac{d|G|}{|G|}$$

(by the Equation of State)

$$= nT \ln \frac{|G_2|}{|G_1|}$$

$$= T \left\{ S\left(|G_2|, \frac{1}{T}\right) - S\left(|G_1|, \frac{1}{T}\right) \right\},$$

i.e. by the difference of the bound energies corresponding to the thermodynamical states $(|G_2|, 1/T)$ and $(|G_1|, 1/T)$. (See Note 23.4.)

References

The computation of the pressure and the formulation of the First and Second Laws (including the definitions of the basic concepts) are essentially due to Khinchin [23]. A slightly different derivation of the Equation of State is given in the paper

[46] KURTH, R., Die Zustandsgleichung der klassischen statistischen Mechanik, *Arch. Rat. Mech. Anal.*, **2**, 32–90, 1958.

On a further application of the Virial Theorem (van der Waals's equation of state) see, for example, Boltzmann [24].

A thorough and severe critique of Boltzmann's Postulate has been given by Khinchin [23], with which the present author agrees completely. Planck's attempt to prove Boltzmann's Postulate has already been rightly criticized by Fowler [31]. Nevertheless, that argument is still standard in textbooks and lecture courses.

SUBJECT INDEX

absolutely continuous 36
    additive 36
addition (of sets) 4
additive class 5
    set function 36
aggregate 4
almost all 33
approximation theorem 31, 35, 131
associative 5
asymptotic integration 159
average (phase) 73, 121
    (time) 66, 115

Banach space 106
Birkhoff's theorems 71, 74
bi-uniform 8
Boltzmann's equation 98
    Law 130, 134
    Postulate 173
Borel–Heine theorem 13
Borel-measurable 30
Borel set 11
bound energy 158
boundary point 11
bounded (set) 11

canonic probability density 130
    truncated 153
Cartesian product 4
Cauchy sequence 40, 106
closed 11
closure 11
commutative 5
complement 4
complementary subspace 10
complete 106
component 9, 10
conditional expectation value 90
    probability 90
configuration 167
    probability 167
continuity theorem 101
continuous 16
    , absolutely 36
correlation coefficient 124
covering theorem 13
cylinder set 10

Darboux sum 29
decomposible, metrically 74
density (mass) 100, 142
    (number) 100, 142
    , partial 149
    (probability) 79
determinant, Jacobian 53, 88
diameter 144
difference (of sets) 4
differential equations 1, 18
distance 10
distribution (of probability) 79
distributive 5

element 3
empty set 3
energy 51
    , bound 158
    , free 158
    , integral 50
    , internal 154
    , kinetic 51
    , potential 51
ensemble 77
entropy 156, 173
enumerable 4
equation of state 147, 149
equations of motion 47
equilibrium, statistical 111
equipartition of energy 147
    of probability 82
equipartition theorem 147
equivalence of components 124
    of functions 41
    of particles 98
ergodic hypothesis 73
essentially different 41
Euler's equations 101
    identity 64
existence theorem 19
expectation value, conditional 90

fictitious ensemble 77
finite 4
First Integral 49
First Law of Thermodynamics 156
flow 48
    , stationary 49

force 48
free energy 158
frequency 77
Fubini's theorem 37
function 7, 36
  , bi-uniform 8
  , continuous 16
  , homogeneous 64
  , inverse 8
  , measurable 29
  , piecewise constant 31

gas 2, 158, 172
Gibbs's canonic probability density
      130
  ensemble 77
  function 167, 173
  H-theorem 171
globular star cluster 83

Hamiltonian equations 49
  function 49
  system 49
harmonic oscillator 123, 148
heat 155
Heine–Borel theorem 13
Hilbert space 39
homogeneous (function) 64
Hopf's theorems 60, 62
H-theorem 171

ideal gas 2, 158, 172
image 8
infinite 4
initial value problem 104
inner measure 25
integral
  , First 49
  , indefinite 36
  , Lebesgue 29, 35
  , lower 29
  , Riemann 30
  , upper 29
integration, asymptotic 159
internal energy 154
intersection 4
interval 11
invariant function 49
  set 57
inverse function 8

Jacobian determinant 53, 88
Jacobi's theorem 65

kinetic energy 51

lacking reason 82
Lagrange's identity 64
Laplace's asymptotic integration 159
law of large numbers 126
laws of thermodynamics 156, 162
Lebesgue integral 29, 35
  measurable function 29
  measure 25
  set 25
limiting element 43
  point 10
linear harmonic oscillator 123, 148
linear space 38
  subset 43
  subspace 43
Liouville's equation 93
  theorem 56, 83
Lipschitz condition 19, 107
lower integral 29

macroscopic state 110, 112, 168
mapping 7, 8, 53
  , bi-uniform 8
  , continuous 16
  , into 7
  , on 8
  , topological 16
mass 48
mass density 142
mass-point 48
mean pressure 143
  temperature 146
  velocity 101
measurable function 29
measure 24
  inner 25
  Lebesgue 25
  outer 24
  Peano 28
  Riemann 28
mechanical system 1, 47
Menge 3
metric space 105
metrically decomposible 74
microscopic state 47, 111
moment of momentum 51
momentum 50, 51

neighbourhood 10, 43
v. Neumann's theorems 66, 68
Newtonian equations 50
  systems 50
norm 40, 105
number density 100, 142
  space 10

open set 10
ordinary differential equations 18
orthogonal 40
oscillator, harmonic 123, 148
outer measure 24

partial density 149
  pressure 101
  temperature 149
particle 48
partition integral 155
Peano's measure 28
period, relative 72
phase average 73, 121
  flow 48
  function 72
  mapping 53
  point 1, 48
  space 1, 48
  trajectory 49
piecewise constant 31
Poincaré's recurrence theorem 57
point 10
  , boundary 11
  , limiting 10
postulates 47, 78
potential 50
  energy 51
  function 50
  , thermodynamical 154
practical certainty 80
pressure 142
  , mean 143
  , partial 101
  tensor 101, 142
principle of sufficient (lacking) reason
    82
probability 73, 77, 78
  density 79
  distribution 79
  distribution, canonic 130
product, Cartesian 4
  , scalar 9
proper extremum 114
  subset 3

rational numbers 6
real space 48
reason, sufficient (lacking) 82
Recurrence theorem 57
relative period 72
  Verweilzeit 72
Riemann integral 30
  measure 28

scalar 9
  product 9
Schwarz' inequality 11, 40

Second Law of Thermodynamics 156
sequence 4
  , finite 4
  , infinite 4
set 3
  , Borel 11
  , bounded 11
  , closed 11
  , cylinder 10
  , enumerable 4
  , finite 4
  , function 36
  , infinite 4
  , Lebesgue 25
  , open 10
  of rational numbers 6
  , Riemann 28
space 4
  , Banach 106
  , complete 106
  , Hilbert 39
  , linear 38
  , metric 105
  , real 48
special sum function 124
star cluster, globular 83
state, macroscopic 110, 112, 168
  , microscopic 47, 111
  , stationary 111
  of statistical equilibrium 111
  , thermodynamical 157
stationary 49
statistical equilibrium 111
statistically stationary 111
streaming velocity 101
subset 3
  , linear 43
  , proper 3
subspace 10
  , complementary 10
  , linear 43
subtraction (of sets) 4
sufficient reason 82
sum (of sets) 4
sum function 124
system, mechanical 1, 46

temperature 146
  , mean 146
  , partial 149
  tensor 146
thermodynamical function 154
  laws 156, 162
  potential 155
  probability 169
  state 154
  variable 154
Third Law of Thermodynamics 162

time average 66, 115
  axis 48
  scale 110
topological mapping 16
total momentum 51
  moment of momentum 51
trajectory 49
transform 104
triangular inequality 12, 40, 106
truncated canonic density 153
Tschebyscheff's inequality 121

uniformly continuous 16
uniqueness theorem 19

upper integral 29

variance 122
vector 9
vector space 1, 10
velocity space 48
Verweilzeit 72
Virial theorem 149

Weierstrass' Approximation Theorem
    131
work 155

Zusammenfassung 3, 8